SERIES

Meet Our Friends

by

William H. Burton, Clara Belle Baker
and Grace K. Kemp

Illustrations by

Janet Ross *and* Raymon Naylor

THE BOBBS-MERRILL COMPANY, INC.

INDIANAPOLIS   NEW YORK

Stories

Around Pine Square

Out in Woodsfield

On Wheels and Wings

Copyright 1950
By The Bobbs-Merrill Company, Inc.
Printed in the United States of America
NR-853

Over the Countryside

In Storyland—New Stories

In Storyland—Old Stories

Around Pine Square

The Ice Cream Man

The children were playing in the park
at Pine Square. Some of them were looking
for the ice cream man.

They liked the ice cream man. They liked
to see his red and white cart.

Every day the ice cream man wheeled
his cart to the park. Every day he came
to find children playing there.

"Let's play tag," said Jean.

"Yes, yes," cried the other children.
"Let's play tag."

"One, two, three, out," said Don.
"One, two, three, out."

All were out but Teddy. Teddy was It.
"Run, run," shouted George. "Keep away
from Teddy. He will tag you."

Away the children ran, and Lucky ran
after them. Lucky was George's dog.

3

Teddy caught Jean. Then Jean started
to run after the children. "Jean is It,"
they cried.

Jean ran after Don, but could not tag
him. Then she began to run after George,
but could not tag him.

At last she caught up with Lucky. "Now
Lucky is It," she laughed.

Lucky ran round and round the park
after the children.

All at once they heard something coming
down the street. They heard ting-a-ling,
ting-a-ling, ting-a-ling.

"Oh, the ice cream man," cried Don.
"I hear the ting-a-ling of his cart."

The children ran fast down the street
to the red and white cart. Lucky ran
down the street with them.

Don and Peggy got some ice cream.
Jean got some ice cream.

"Teddy and I cannot get ice cream,"
said George. "Mother could not give us
money for ice cream."

"She did not have much money at home
today," said Teddy.

"Let me get you ice cream," said Don.

Don got ice cream for George and Teddy.
"Thank you very much," they said.

"Bow-wow-wow," cried Lucky.

"Lucky wants ice cream," said Jean.

Jean got ice cream for Lucky.

6

Lucky was a happy, happy dog. He liked
ice cream as much as the children did.
He often ate with the children.

"Now let's play tag again," said Peggy.
"Let's go back to the park at Pine Square
and play tag again."

The ice cream man went down the street.
The children heard him going on his way,
ting-a-ling, ting-a-ling, ting-a-ling.

At the Firehouse

One day Peggy and Jean went to play
with Ann and Linda. Ann and Linda lived
next to a firehouse in Pine Square.

"The men are here today," said Peggy
as she looked in the firehouse.

"Yes, the men are here, ready to go
to a fire," said Jean. "They are ready
for someone to call them."

The firemen had a little pet monkey
called Peanuts. The pet monkey liked
to live at the firehouse.

Much of the time he lived in a box,
but the firemen often let him out. Then
they caught him and put him back.

He had a big fire hat that he liked
to put on. Often he put on the hat and
played that he was a fireman.

Peggy and Jean saw him with his hat
as they went by the firehouse.

Ann was in the yard when the girls came
to see her. "Hello," said Jean. "We came
over to play. Where is Linda?"

"Linda is asleep," said Ann. "Every day
after dinner she has to sleep for a while.
She is not big like us, you know."

The girls began to play in the yard
with Ann's doll and cart. After a while
they began to watch the firemen.

"Let's see what the firemen are doing
next door," said Jean.

The firemen saw the girls and called,
"Why not come over here for a while?
Come to play with our pet monkey."

The firemen were working on a truck.
They were washing the truck to make it
ready for a fire.

Peanuts began to wash Ann's little cart.
He started to wash her doll.

"When we wash the big truck, he wants
to wash things, too," said a fireman.

Ann ran to get her doll from the cart.
"I do not want Peanuts to wash my doll,"
she said. Then they all laughed.

By and by Peanuts went up a big tree
by the firehouse. He looked all around
from the big tree.

Suddenly he came down fast and ran
into the firehouse. He put on his fire hat
and started down the street.

A fireman ran after him, but on he went.
He would not come back.

"Fire!" shouted the fireman suddenly.
"Peanuts is going to a fire."

The other firemen jumped on the truck.
The three girls heard the truck go away
with a loud, loud noise.

Suddenly the loud noise came to a stop.
"Let's go to the fire," said Jean.

"Oh, no, we cannot go to the fire,"
said Ann. "Children only get in the way
when they go to a fire."

"Then let's watch here for the firemen
to come back," said Peggy.

They looked and looked down the street,
but they could not see the firemen. Where
were the firemen? Where was Peanuts?

In a little while the firemen came back with their truck. They jumped down fast and took off their raincoats.

"Our pet monkey is a fireman now," said one of the men. "He took us to a fire that he saw from the tree."

"Are you going to give him a prize for helping you?" asked Ann.

"Yes, girls, let's give him a prize," said another fireman. "Take this money and get him a bag of peanuts."

The three girls took the money and ran off to a store. Then what fun they had helping Peanuts eat his prize!

The Little Store

At Pine Square was a little store where Peter helped his father. He liked to work in the store.

Sometimes he helped to wash windows. At other times he helped people to find things like apples and bread.

One day when Peter was in the store, his father was in a back room. He had work to do there.

Peter began to open a box. "I will put some cans in the window," he said.

He took cans from the box and made a kind of tent in the window. "This is a very good tent," he said.

Just then the door opened, ting-a-ling,
ting-a-ling, and Don came into the store.
His dog, Buster, came in, too.

"No, no, Buster, you cannot come in,"
said Peter. "Go outside."

Buster did not go outside. He just began
to run around the store. Suddenly he ran
into the big tent of cans.

Crash! Crash! Crash! Down came the tent
of cans all around him. Down it crashed
with a loud, loud noise.

What a funny, funny picture Buster made
with cans all around him!

Peter's father heard the crashing noise
and came hurrying in. He could not tell
what the crashing noise was.

"What made the loud crash?" he called.
"Are you hurt? Are you hurt?"

Just then he saw Buster under the cans
and began to laugh.

Buster was not hurt by the crashing cans, but he wanted to get away. He jumped up and ran to the door.

"Buster wants to get out," said Peter. "Let him get out, Don."

Don opened the door, ting-a-ling-ling, and Buster ran out as fast as he could go. He ran all the way home.

"Oh, Father," said Peter. "I wanted you to see the tent of cans in the window. Let me make a new tent."

"May I help?" asked Don. "After all, my dog knocked the old tent down."

"Let's all help to make the new tent," said Peter's father.

They began to make a new tent of cans in the window. They put one can on another to make the new tent.

"What a good tent!" said Don. "The cans go up, up, and around."

"Buster will not knock this tent down," said Peter. "He will not come to the store again for a long time."

"No, he will not knock this tent down," laughed Don. "He did not have much fun while he was here today."

Sick with a Cold

Peter lived with his father and mother over the little store. Outside the store were stairs going up to their home.

One day Peter came home from school sick. He was sick with a cold.

The next day his birthday was coming, and he wanted to have fun.

"Oh, my!" he said. "Here I am sick, and my birthday is coming."

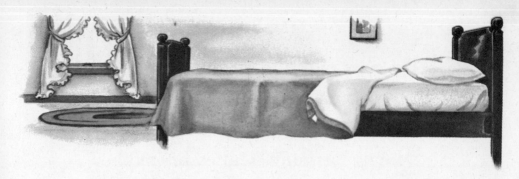

When Peter's mother saw him coming
up the stairs, she asked, "Are you hurt?
Are you sick?"

"I have caught a cold," said Peter.
"I am sick with a cold."

"Let me help you get ready for bed,"
said his mother. "Go to bed for a while,
and soon you will be better."

"Yes, I want to be better by morning,"
said Peter. "I do not want to be sick
on my birthday."

"Go to bed and sleep," said his mother.
"Sleep is good for a cold."

Peter was soon in his bed fast asleep.
He was fast asleep when his father came
upstairs from the store.

The next morning when Peter woke up,
he was better, but he could not get up.
He had to stay in bed.

"Happy birthday," called his mother
as she came into the room.

"Not a very happy birthday," said Peter.
"Here I am sick in bed with a cold."

"Yes, you will have to stay in bed,"
said his mother.

"I did not want to stay in bed today,"
said Peter. "I wanted to go to school
on my birthday."

Peter went back to sleep for a while.
When he woke up, he was much better.

Soon after he awoke, he wanted to play.
He wanted to play on the bed with some
of his toys.

"Mother," he called. "Please bring me
some toys. I want to play with them
here on the bed."

His mother came to the bed with a box
of new blocks. "Here is a birthday present
for you," she said.

"New blocks!" said Peter. "New blocks
for a birthday present! Thank you."

Peter took the blocks and began to play
with them on his bed. By and by he said,
"See my block city."

"Oh, good," said his mother. "Let's play
that we live in the block city."

Then Peter and his mother played that
they lived in the block city. What fun
they had with the blocks!

After a while Peter heard some children
down the street. "Oh, school is just out,"
he said to his mother.

The children came to a stop by the store
and looked up at his window. They shouted,
"Hello, Peter," and sang:

     "Happy birthday to you.

     Happy birthday to you.

     Happy birthday, friend Peter.

     Happy birthday to you."

Suddenly Peter forgot that he was sick.
He jumped out of bed and ran to the window
to look down at his friends.

"Hello, hello," he called. "Thank you
for coming to see me."

"We hope that you will be better soon,"
shouted Don. "We hope that you can come
to school again soon."

"I am much better now," called Peter.
"I hope to be out in a day or two."

"Good-by," shouted the children.

"Good-by," Peter called back.

After his friends went on, Peter said, "Mother, may I stay up for a while now? I am much better."

"Yes, you may stay up for a while now," said his mother. "You look better."

That night Peter's father brought up some ice cream. He brought it upstairs and put it on a table.

Peter went out to the table. How good the ice cream was!

"I was sick on my birthday, but I had fun after all," he said at the table.

"You brought me a box of blocks, and you brought me ice cream," he went on. "My friends sang under my window."

Here Comes the Bus

The twins, Jack and Mack, were playing
in the house. Their mother was going
to the store on a bus.

She was in a big hurry to get started,
for the bus would come soon. She wanted
to be ready when it came.

First she put on her good black hat.
Then she looked for her white gloves,
but could not find them.

"Come, Jack and Mack," she called.
"Please help me to find my white gloves,
or I shall miss the bus."

"Where did you put your white gloves?"
asked the two boys.

"Here on this table," said their mother.
"I just put them here with my black hat,
and now they are gone."

The twins looked all around the table
and all around the room. "We cannot find
your white gloves," they said.

"Then I must hurry on without them,"
said their mother. "I must be on my way,
or the bus will be gone."

She went out of the house and started
down the street. "Good-by, good-by,"
she called to the twins.

"Good-by, Mother," they called back,
watching from the window. Then they
waved, and she waved.

Suddenly Jack said, "Look, Mack. What
are those things on Mother's hat?"

"Those are white flowers," said Mack.
"She has white flowers on her hat."

"They look like white gloves to me,"
said Jack. "They are not flowers."

Mack looked again at the hat and said,
"Those white things are Mother's gloves.
Her gloves are on her hat."

"We must tell her," called out Jack.
"Let's hurry or she will be gone."

The twins ran as fast as they could
from the house. They waved their hands
and shouted as they went.

Their dogs started to bark and run
after them. The dogs barked and barked.

What a loud noise they all made!

"Look on your hat, Mother," cried Mack as he ran down the street.

"Yes, look on your hat," cried Jack.

Their mother put up her hands to see what was there. Much to her surprise, she held gloves in her hands.

Just then the bus came, and she had to get on. When the bus started away, she held her gloves in the window.

As she held up the gloves, she began to laugh. The twins began to laugh, too, and the dogs started to bark.

Everyone was happy!

Black Pepper

Most of the children at Pine Square had good pets. Peter had a black dog for a pet. His dog's name was Black Pepper.

Black Pepper did good tricks for Peter. Most of the time he liked to do tricks, but sometimes he did not.

"Come here, Pepper," said Peter one day. "Come and do tricks for me."

Pepper just looked at Peter and started to go up the stairs. He did not want to do tricks that day.

"Oh, my," said Peter. "In the morning we are going to have a dog show. I hope that you will do your tricks then."

The next morning all the boys brought their dogs to Don's yard. Every dog sat on a box for the show.

Most of the children near by came to see the dogs speak, jump, and do other tricks. They hoped to see a good show.

First, Don had Buster do some tricks for the children. He pulled out a wagon and said, "Jump, Buster."

Buster went over the wagon. He went over it again and again.

"Now speak, Buster, speak," said Don. Then Buster barked and barked.

Next Don asked Buster to roll over, and Buster rolled over and over.

The boys and girls clapped their hands as Buster did one trick after another. They clapped and clapped.

When Buster sat down on his box again, George asked Lucky to do tricks.

Lucky sat up, and then he rolled over for George. He rolled over and over.

"Speak," said George, and Lucky barked time and again.

"Go to sleep for a while," said George, and Lucky played that he was asleep.

"Now, Lucky, get up and wave good-by to the children," said George.

Then Lucky waved good-by. This was his very best trick. The children clapped and clapped and clapped.

The next dog was Black Pepper. "Come
and do your tricks," said Peter.

Peter held three things in his hands,
a ball, a stick, and some paper. First,
he put down the ball.

Then he said, "Get the ball, Pepper.
Get it and bring it to me."

Pepper did not get the ball for Peter.
He just looked and started away.

"Come back here, Pepper," called Peter.
"Come and get the ball."

Pepper came back, but he did not get
the ball. He just barked.

"Pepper is not good today," said Peter. "He will not do his tricks."

Peter put Black Pepper back on his box, and the show went on.

Jack and Mack had Teeny and Weeny do tricks for the children. They put down a little toy fence.

Jack had Teeny jump over the toy fence. Then Mack had Weeny jump over it.

They had the dogs speak and roll over for the children. Last they asked them to go after a stick.

Teeny and Weeny ran to get the stick
and brought it back to the boys.

The children clapped their hands to see
the little dogs do their tricks.

Now the show was over. "We want to see
some more tricks," said Ann. "Let's see
what Black Pepper will do."

"Yes, yes," cried the other children.
"Maybe he will do his tricks now."

Peter asked Black Pepper to jump down
from his box. Once more he held the ball,
the stick, and the paper.

"Bring the paper to me," said Peter.
Pepper brought the paper.

"Bring the stick to me," said Peter.
Pepper picked up the stick.

"Now bring the ball to me," said Peter.
Pepper came back with the ball.

Peter put all three things down again, the ball, the stick, and the paper. "Now get all of them at once," he said.

Pepper picked up the ball. Then he went over to the paper, but could not get it. He could not pick it up.

Everyone watched. What would he do? How would he get the paper?

Here is what Pepper did. He put down the ball. Then he picked up the paper, next the stick, and last the ball.

"Good!" cried Peter. "You did it!"

Pepper barked and ran back to his box. How the children clapped for him!

Jean and the Funny Animals

Jean's aunt was staying overnight
with her. "Tomorrow let's go to the park,"
said her aunt as Jean went to bed.

"I think that will be fun," said Jean.
"Is there a merry-go-round at the park
with animals on it?"

"All kinds of animals," said her aunt.
"You will see a horse, a pony, a rabbit,
a fox, a bear, and an elephant."

"Oh, funny circus animals," said Jean.
"Most of those are circus animals."

Jean went to sleep. By and by she began
to dream that it was tomorrow. She was
at the big city park.

"I think that I'll get peanuts to eat
in the park," she said.

She got a bag of peanuts and went on
to the merry-go-round. There she saw
all kinds of animals.

First she saw a horse, a pony, a rabbit,
a fox, a bear, and an elephant. Then last
she saw an old brown lion.

"Here are almost all kinds of animals,"
said Jean. "First, I think that I'll ride
the elephant or the old brown lion."

She was almost up to the merry-go-round
when the elephant jumped off. He put out
his trunk for some peanuts.

Jean gave him some of her peanuts. Then
he put out his trunk for more. He wanted
more and more of her peanuts.

"What shall I do?" she asked.

She left the elephant and walked away.
He could not have all her peanuts.

Soon she heard a noise. She looked back
and saw the elephant coming after her.

Next came the horse. Then came the pony,
the rabbit, the fox, and the bear. Last there
came the old brown lion.

"Why, this is almost like a circus parade,"
said Jean with a smile.

She sat down, and all the funny animals
sat down by her. They sat down and ate
most of her peanuts.

At last she had only one peanut left.
As she took the last peanut from her bag,
the elephant put out his trunk.

"Oh, no, I have only one peanut left,"
she said. "This one is for me."

She got up and ran to a big tree. Round
and round she went, and the animals came
round and round after her.

Again the elephant was first. Then came
the horse, the pony, the rabbit, the fox,
the bear, and the old brown lion.

The animals almost caught up with Jean.
Just then she heard someone call to her,
"Jean, it is time to get up."

She sat up in bed and looked around.
The funny animals were gone.

"Come and get up now," said her aunt.
"We are going to the park today."

"We cannot ride on the merry-go-round,"
said Jean. "The funny animals jumped off
and ran after me."

"I think that you have had a dream,"
said her aunt with a smile.

Jean climbed out of bed and dressed fast
for breakfast. Then she and her aunt left
for the big city park.

When they came to the big park, she got
some peanuts. "I must have some peanuts
for the funny animals," she said.

She held the bag in her hands and ran
to a big tree to find the animals. "Oh,"
she cried. "The animals are gone!"

She went on fast to the merry-go-round
to look for the animals. There they were,
going round and round.

High on the merry-go-round she saw
the horse, pony, rabbit, fox, and bear.
Last she saw the elephant and lion.

"The funny animals have climbed back,
high on the merry-go-round," she said.

She held out a peanut to the elephant,
but he did not put out his trunk for it.
He did not want the peanut.

He just went round and round and round,
with all the funny animals. Round he went,
high on the merry-go-round.

While Jean was looking at the animals, her aunt came and asked, "What animal do you wish to ride first? Would you like a big animal or a little one?"

"I think that I'll ride a little animal like the rabbit or the fox first," said Jean. "After that I'll ride a big circus animal like the elephant or the lion."

Jean climbed on the rabbit's back and went round and round. She went round time and time again.

When the merry-go-round came to a stop, Jean climbed down from the rabbit's back. "Now do you wish to ride a circus animal?" asked her aunt.

"Yes, I want to ride the big old elephant if I can climb on his high back," said Jean. "He ran after me in my dream last night, but he is good today."

Jean asked her aunt to help her climb on the elephant's back. Then she began to go round and round, and up and down. The elephant gave her a good ride.

"Do not walk off the merry-go-round, as you did in my funny dream," she said. "I cannot stay on your back if you walk off the merry-go-round now."

The big old elephant did not walk off. He just stayed where he was, with Jean on his back. He went round and round, and up and down for a long ride.

Merry-Go-Round

I climbed up on the merry-go-round,
And it went round and round.
I climbed up on a big brown horse,
And it went up and down.

> Around and round
> And up and down,
> Around and round
> And up and down.
> I sat high up
> On a big brown horse
> And rode around
> On the merry-go-round
> And rode around.

On the merry-go-round
I rode around,
On the merry-go-round
Around and round and round.

Out in Woodsfield

Off to a New Home

One day George and Teddy helped to get ready to move. Their father had new work in a town called Woodsfield.

"I wish that we did not have to move away from Pine Square," said George.

"I wish that all our friends could move away with us," said Teddy. "We shall miss all our friends here."

"Yes, we shall miss them," said George.

"You soon will make some new friends after we move," said their mother.

"Not many people live in Woodsfield,"
said George. "There are not many streets
and not very many houses. Woodsfield is
only a small town."

"Yes, Woodsfield is only a small town,
but you will like it," said his mother.
"You will have fun there."

"Will we have more room for play there?"
asked Teddy. "Will we have a big yard
around our house?"

"Yes, you will have much more room,"
said his mother. "Almost all the houses
in small towns have big yards."

"It will be fun to live where we have
a big yard," said Teddy.

The next morning men came to the house
to move things. They parked a big truck
a little way from the house.

George and Teddy watched the men carry
things from the house. They watched them
put things in the big truck.

Lucky ran here and there to watch, too.
He ran up and down the stairs. He jumped
in and out of the truck. He could not tell
what the men were doing.

After a while there was not a thing left
in the house. The men jumped on the truck
and shouted, "Good-by now. We are off
to the town of Woodsfield."

Don and Peggy came over to say good-by. Jack and Mack came, and Ann and Linda. Peter came and Jean came. All came to say good-by to George and Teddy.

They came to say good-by to Lucky, too. "Good-by, old friend," they said.

George and Teddy got in the automobile with their father and mother. They rode in the back with Lucky. Soon they were off on their way to Woodsfield.

They waved from the automobile window, and the children waved back at them.

The boys liked their automobile ride over the country road. They saw all kinds of things along the road.

The road went by many big farms. Often the boys waved at children on the farms, and Lucky barked at farm animals.

Every once in a while the road came to a small town. When the boys saw a town, they would say, "Daddy, are we there? Is this Woodsfield?"

Then every time their father would say, "Oh, no, this is not Woodsfield." By and by he smiled and said, "The next town will be Woodsfield. We are almost there."

Soon they came to Main Street and rode by houses with big yards. Next they came to two blocks of stores.

A little way from the stores they left Main Street and went along a side street. Here they came to their new home.

"What a big, wide yard!" cried the boys. "Is the big, wide yard all ours?"

"Yes, the big, wide yard is all ours," laughed their father. "Jump out and see how you like it."

The big truck was there with the things for the house. The men on the truck put all the things in place in the rooms. Then they said good-by and rode away.

The boys went from room to room to look at the house. Lucky ran here and there to see the house, too.

"Oh, Mother, the men forgot to put up our bed," called the boys. "Now we have no place to sleep."

"Daddy and I have a surprise for you," said their mother.

After a while a truck came from a store on Main Street. Then two men jumped out and brought in some bunk beds.

"Bunk beds!" shouted George and Teddy. "Now we have bunk beds to take the place of our old, wide bed. One of us can sleep up high, and the other down under."

Finding New Friends

George and Teddy looked out the window of their new home. They saw four children, two boys and two girls, near the house.

"Look, Mother, four children are coming to the house," they cried.

Just then they heard a knock at the door. Next they heard someone call out, "Please may we say hello to you? We just came to say hello."

"Hello," said George and Teddy.

"Yes, hello there," said the boys' mother. "Come in for a little while. We are happy to see some new friends."

The four children came into the house.
One of the girls said, "My name is Jean,
and this is Jack. We live down the street
from your house."

The other girl said, "My name is Linda,
and this is Timmie. Timmie and I live
next to Jack and Jean."

George said, "We are happy to know you.
My name is George, and this is Teddy."

"Bow-wow, bow-wow," barked Lucky,
looking up at George.

"Oh, yes," said George. "This is Lucky.
He lives here, too."

"May I pet Lucky?" asked Timmie.

"Yes, you may pet him," said George.
"He will not hurt you."

"Would you like to play a game of tag with us?" asked Teddy.

"Yes," cried the children. "Let's play a game of tag."

The children ran to play a game of tag, and Lucky ran after them. "Bow-wow," he barked as he ran.

"First, we must pick someone to be It," cried Jack. "Who will be It?"

"I'll be It," said Jean.

The children ran away from Jean. Soon she caught Teddy, and he caught Linda. The game went on and on.

"When we played tag at Pine Square, we played in a city park," said George. "Here we play in a big, wide yard."

After the game was over, Timmie said,
"I like you, George and Teddy."

"All of us like you, George and Teddy,"
said Linda. "Tomorrow come over to play
in our yard."

"Yes, tomorrow is Saturday," said Jack.
"Saturday is a good day to play games,
for there is no school."

"Thank you," said George and Teddy.
"If we cannot come over tomorrow, maybe
we can come over next week. We can play
after school some day next week."

"Bring Lucky with you," said Timmie.

George and Teddy went into the house with their father and mother. "We like our new friends here," they said.

"Good!" said their father. "We hoped that you would like them."

"How funny!" said Teddy. "We played with a Jack, a Jean, and a Linda today. Three of our friends at Pine Square have those first names, too."

"Yes," smiled George. "Now we know two Jacks, two Jeans, and two Lindas."

That night the boys got ready to sleep in their new bunk beds. "Who is going to sleep in the high bed?" asked Teddy. "Will you sleep up there?"

"No," said George. "We can take turns sleeping up there if you wish. You take your turn up there this week, and I'll sleep in the low bed. Then next week you take your turn in the low bed."

The boys climbed into their bunk beds,
Teddy the high one, and George the low one.
"Good night," Teddy called down to George
in the low bed.

"Good night, up there," George called
to Teddy in the high bed. "Do not roll out
in the night."

Then Teddy said, "George, do you know
that we may like it in Woodsfield?"

"Yes," George called back. "I think that
we shall like it here."

Soon the boys were fast asleep.

Along Main Street

How strange things were to the boys when
they woke up the next morning. They were
in strange bunk beds, in a strange room,
in a strange house.

"How did you like your new bunk beds?"
asked their mother at breakfast.

"They were strange beds to sleep in, but
we liked them," said George. "Teddy had
the high bunk, and I the low bunk."

"It was fun to sleep in the high bunk
last night," said Teddy.

"Next week it will be my turn to sleep
in the high bunk," said George.

The boys ate breakfast and ran outside to play with Lucky. They played and played in the big, wide yard.

By and by they ran out to the sidewalk to look up and down the street. "Things are just as strange out here as in the house," said George. "Everything is strange."

"Maybe we can go to see Jack and Jean, or Linda and Timmie," said Teddy.

"Come for a walk along Main Street," called their mother. "Today is Saturday, and I must get groceries."

"Oh, good!" cried Teddy. "We'll have fun going for a walk along Main Street. We'll carry your groceries home."

As they started, Jack and Jean called
to them, "Where are you going?"

"Oh, we are on our way to Main Street
for groceries," said George.

"Come over and play when you get back
from Main Street," said Jack. "Saturday is
a good day for play. We can play all day
in our yard."

"Thank you," said George. "We'll come
to play when we get back."

"Let Lucky come," called Jean. "We want
to play with him, too."

They walked on for almost two blocks. "Must we turn at the next corner to get to Main Street?" asked George.

"Yes, we must turn at the next corner," said his mother.

Soon they came to the corner and turned on Main Street. "See all the automobiles and people," cried Teddy. "Why are there so many people here today?"

"Most of the people are farmers who live near by," said his mother. "On Saturdays most of them stop work and come to town. Saturday is a good day for stores to sell things to farmers."

"The stores at Pine Square do not sell things to farmers," said Teddy.

"No, the stores there sell things only to city people," said his mother. "There are no farmers around those stores, but there are farmers all around here."

"Here is a store that sells groceries,"
said George on Main Street.

They went in, and the store people said,
"Good morning."

"Do the people know you?" asked Teddy.
"They speak as if they know you."

"No," said his mother. "They do not know
me, but they want to be friends."

A man came to get groceries for them
in the store. He went here and there to get
packages and cans.

"Now let me put the packages and cans
in your basket," said the man.

George and Teddy watched the store man put the packages and cans in the basket. "You are new to our store," he smiled. "Have you just moved here?"

"Yes, we have just moved to Woodsfield," said the boys' mother.

"Well, then, let me give the two boys some peanuts," he said. "We like to give children presents the first time they come to our store."

"The man looked after us very well," said the boys' mother on the way home.

"Yes, he gave us peanuts," said Teddy.

Groceries

The store around the corner
Has groceries to sell.
I go there with my mother;
I like that very well.

We look in the store windows
As we walk down the street.
We bring home many packages
Of groceries to eat.

First Day at School

Monday morning George woke up early
in his high bunk. The next week had come,
and it was his turn to sleep up high.
"Come, Teddy," he said. "This is Monday,
and we must dress in a hurry."

"Monday," said Teddy as he jumped out
to dress. "Why hurry today? Oh, I know.
Today we start to school."

"Yes, Daddy will go with us to help us
on our first day," said George.

After breakfast the boys got ready
to start. They jumped in the automobile
and soon were on their way. "Good-by,"
they called to their mother.

Down the street on a corner they saw
Jack, Jean, and Linda. "Come and ride
with us," said George and Teddy.

The three children were happy to ride
with George and Teddy. "We thank you
for asking us," they said.

"Where is Timmie today?" asked Teddy.
"Why is he not here?"

"Oh, Timmie is at home," said Linda.
"He is too little for school."

The school was only four blocks away. When George saw the building, he said, "What a pretty school!"

"What a pretty green yard!" said Teddy. "See how green everything is!"

"Yes, we like our pretty green yard," said Linda. "Back of the building we have a good place to play."

"Let's go back there to play for a while," said Jack and Jean.

"We wish that we could, but we must go into the building first," said George. "We want to find our rooms."

The two boys and their father went on into the building. There George found that he would be in Miss Long's room. Teddy went to Miss Green's room.

As soon as the boys found their rooms, their father went on his way. By and by all the children came into the building. It was time for school.

In her room Miss Long said, "Children, let us say hello to our new friend, George. This is his first day here."

"Hello, George," cried the children.

In her room Miss Green said, "Teddy, come, write your name for us. Write it in big letters for us."

The children clapped and clapped.

George and Teddy liked their first day at the Woodsfield school. Everyone was kind to them. Everyone wanted to help them get a good start.

After school when the boys went home,
they found their mother at the door.
"Well, boys," she said. "How do you like
your new school?"

"Oh, we like it," said George. "I am
in Miss Long's room."

"I go to Miss Green," said Teddy.

"Let's write a letter to our old friends
at Pine Square," said George. "Let's write
about our new home and school."

"Yes, let's go upstairs to write a letter,"
said Teddy. "We can write a good letter
about things here."

74

The boys went to their room to write a letter to their old friends in the city. This is what they said.

To Our Friends at Pine Square,

We like our home and school here. At first things were very strange to us, but now they are not.

Write us a letter about everything at Pine Square. Please write soon.

George and Teddy

Little Lost Cat

One morning after Linda went to school,
Timmie began to look for his little cat.
"I'll play with my cat while Linda is
at school," he said.

His cat was not there. "My cat is lost,"
he said. "She is lost, and I must hurry
to find her."

He looked in the house, and he looked
in the yard, but he could not find her.
Then he looked along the street.

Down the street a little way was a man.
Timmie walked up to the man and asked,
"Have you seen my cat? She is lost, and
I cannot find her."

"What is your cat like?" asked the man.
"Tell me about her."

"She has little yellow spots all over,"
said Timmie, looking up.

"What? Yellow spots?" said the man.

"Yes, little yellow spots all over,"
said Timmie again.

"Oh, no," laughed the man. "No cat has
little yellow spots all over."

"My cat has," said Timmie.

Soon a woman came along the street.
Timmie walked up to the woman and asked,
"Have you seen my cat? She is lost, and
I cannot find her."

"No, I think not, but tell me about her,"
said the woman.

"She has little yellow spots all over,"
Timmie said to the woman. "Then she has
big ears and a red nose."

The woman began to laugh and said,
"Oh, my, my! No cat could look like that.
No cat has little yellow spots all over.
No cat has big ears and a red nose."

"My cat has," said Timmie. "My cat has
all those things."

Next a big girl came along the street.
Timmie walked up to the girl and asked,
"Have you seen my cat?"

"No, I do not think so," said the girl.
"Tell me about her."

"She has little yellow spots all over,"
said Timmie once more. "She has big ears
and a red nose. Then she has long legs
without feet."

The girl looked down at Timmie and said,
"Why, no cat has little yellow spots all over.
No cat has big ears and a red nose, or
long legs without feet."

"My cat has," said Timmie. "My cat has
all those things."

The man, woman, and girl started away.
"If we see a cat with those funny things,
we'll let you know," they said.

Then Timmie's mother came hurrying down the street. "Timmie," she called. "See what I have found!"

In her hands she had a funny toy cat with little yellow spots all over. It had big ears and a red nose. It had long legs without feet.

The man laughed out loud.

The woman said, "Well, well!"

The big girl said, "What a cat!"

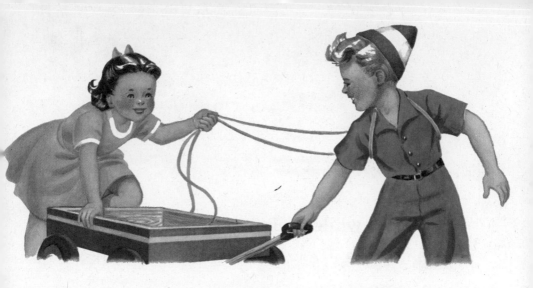

A Strange Kind of Horse

The milkman in Woodsfield had a horse
to pull his wagon. Jack and Jean liked
to watch him drive his horse. They wished
that they could drive a horse, too.

One Saturday Jack said, "Let's play that
I am a horse, hitched to our little wagon.
Then you can drive me."

Jack played that he was a horse, hitched
to the little wagon. Jean rode in the wagon
to drive him along the sidewalk. Then off
they went down the street.

After a while Jack played that he liked
to eat grass. He walked off the sidewalk
for a bite of grass.

Jean did not want him to stop to eat.
"This is no time to eat a bite of grass,"
she said. "You are hitched to a wagon.
Let's go on our way."

Down the street they came to a woman,
waiting on a corner. She had two big bags
of groceries.

"Wait, Jack, wait," said Jean. "Here is
Mrs. Black on the corner."

"I cannot speak, Mrs. Black," said Jack.
"I am a horse, hitched to a wagon."

"A horse!" said Mrs. Black in surprise.

"See me drive my horse," said Jean.
"Let us take your bags of groceries home
in our wagon."

"Thank you," said Mrs. Black. "I am
glad that you came along with your wagon.
My groceries are very heavy."

Mrs. Black put the bags of groceries
in the wagon. Then Jack began to pull
the wagon down the street. Jean walked
beside the wagon to drive him.

Soon they came to Mrs. Black's house.
"I am glad that I did not have to carry
those heavy bags home," she said.

Mrs. Black picked up her bags and said, "What strange ears your horse has, Jean, and what a strange nose. He should have long ears and a long nose."

Jean laughed and laughed.

"Your horse has only two feet and legs," said Mrs. Black next. "He should have four feet and legs."

Then Jean laughed some more.

"What do you like to eat, little horse?" asked Mrs. Black.

"Sometimes I stop for a bite of grass," said Jack, starting to speak.

"Do you like hay?" asked Mrs. Black.

"Not very well," said Jack. "I am not that kind of horse."

"Are you the kind of horse that likes gingerbread cookies?" asked Mrs. Black.

"Gingerbread cookies!" laughed Jack. "Yes, I am that kind of horse."

Mrs. Black asked the two children
to come into her house. She brought out
good gingerbread cookies and milk. "Here
you are," she said.

"I am glad that we came," said Jack.

While they were eating, Jean said, "Now
you see what kind of horse I have. He eats
gingerbread cookies and milk."

"Let us know the next time we can help
you with bags or packages," said Jack.
"I am that kind of horse, too."

Where Is Lucky?

Every day when George and Teddy came
from school, Lucky was waiting for them.
Sometimes he came to the street corner
to meet them. One day he was not waiting,
and he did not come to meet them.

"He should be here," said the two boys.
"Where can he be?"

They went on into the house. "Mother,"
they said. "Have you seen Lucky?"

"No, I have not seen him for a while,"
said their mother.

"Oh, my!" said the boys. "Where is he? What if he is lost or hurt?"

"Maybe he has gone to play with some of your friends," said their mother.

The boys ran down the street to see. "Is Lucky playing with you?" they asked Jack and Jean. "He did not come to meet us after school today."

"No, we have not seen him," said Jack. "Where can he be?"

They ran on to see Linda and Timmie. "Lucky is gone," they called.

Soon all the children began to look for Lucky. They looked and looked, but they could not find him.

George and Teddy ran to their father
when he came from work. "Lucky is gone,"
they said. "He may be lost somewhere, or
he may be hurt."

"What! Lucky gone?" said their father.
"Let's hope that he is not lost or hurt.
After dinner, if he has not come back,
we'll go to look for him."

They went in and sat down at the table,
but no one started to eat much dinner.
They just could not keep from thinking
about Lucky. Where was he? Was he lost?
Was he hurt? Would he come back?

All at once they heard a little noise
upstairs that went scratch, scratch, scratch.
Then they heard the little noise again,
scratch, scratch, scratch.

"What is that little noise?" cried George.
"Can it be Lucky scratching?"

Soon they heard the scratching noise
once more. They jumped up from the table
to see where it came from.

"It comes from our room," said George.

The boys went up the stairs. They ran
fast to their room and looked in the door.
There they found something very funny,
but something that made them very glad.
Lucky was on the high bunk bed.

"Oh, Lucky, how did you get up there?"
asked George. "Do you have wings?"

"Bow-wow, bow-wow," barked Lucky,
as if to say, "No, I do not have wings.
Come to get me down."

"Hurry, Mother and Daddy," cried Teddy.
"Come and see Lucky on the high bunk bed
in our room."

"How strange that he did not go to sleep
in the low bunk bed," said George.

"He just wanted to take turns sleeping
in the high bunk," said his father. Then
everyone laughed.

The two boys ran down the street to tell
all their friends that Lucky was found.
To this day no one knows just how he got
on the high bunk bed. No one knows how
he got up there without wings.

Burning the Greens

By and by winter came to Woodsfield.
The winter days and nights were very cold.
Snow and ice could be seen on the yards
and on the streets.

All the children liked to play outdoors
on the cold days in winter. "I like winter
with its snow and ice," said George.

"Oh, I like winter, too," said Teddy.
"My hands, ears, and nose get cold when
I play outside. My feet and legs get cold,
but I have a good time."

After winter came, the children began
to think of Christmas. Soon the time came
for people to put up their Christmas trees.
Almost everyone had a tree.

George and Teddy had a Christmas tree,
and most of the other children had trees.
Green trees with pretty lights showed
in most of the windows.

The people walked along the streets
at night to see the pretty trees and lights.
They dressed in heavy coats and gloves,
for the winter nights were cold. "We have
our best times at Christmas," they said.

Christmas was a good winter day. When
the people woke up, they found everything
white with snow.

After breakfast George and Teddy heard
a knock at the door. "Merry Christmas!"
called Linda and Timmie.

"Come in to see our Christmas presents,"
said George. "We have some new toys."

The children played with the new toys
for a while. Then they put on their coats
and went to have fun in the snow.

About a week after Christmas was over,
George and Teddy took down their tree.
"What are we going to do with the tree?"
they asked their father.

"We are going to keep it for a party,"
said their father. "Every winter here
the people have a Christmas tree party.
They put their Christmas trees together
and burn them in the park."

"Oh, my!" said George. "The people put
all their trees together and burn them.
What a fire they must have!"

"Yes, they burn all the trees together,"
said his father. "They often speak of it
as the burning of the greens."

"When will they have the big party?"
asked George.

"Next Monday night," said his father.
"Men will come around sometime Monday
to get the trees for the party."

On Monday men came to all the houses with trucks to get the trees for the party. They took the trees to a pretty little park along Main Street.

The children went to the park to watch the men work. They saw them put the trees one over another on the snow.

"How many trees there are together!" said Jack. "They should make a big fire when they start to burn."

"Yes, they should make a pretty light, burning on the white snow," said Linda. "What fun we shall have!"

Early Monday night all the people went
to the park for the burning of the greens.
Men lighted the fire, and soon it jumped
up high. What a pretty picture it made
on the cold winter night!

While the people looked on, they sang
about Christmas. First, the children sang,
and then everyone sang together.

On the way home, George said, "We had
fun tonight. Burning the greens helped
us to have Christmas all over again."

On Wheels and Wings

Off on a Train

The children at Pine Square wished
that they could see George and Teddy.
Time and again Don said, "Please, Daddy,
take us to see George and Teddy."

One day when Daddy came from work,
he said, "I have a surprise for you today.
Saturday morning we'll go to Woodsfield
to see George and Teddy."

"Oh, good!" cried Don and Peggy. "Then
we'll get to see George and Teddy again.
How are we going?"

"We are going on a big railroad train,"
said Daddy with a smile.

Saturday morning everyone got up early and went to the railroad station. "How big the railroad station looks," said Peggy as she went into the building.

Inside the railroad station was a room where people waited for trains. There were little stores and places to eat.

"What are you going to do here, Daddy, in this big place?" asked Don.

"See those small windows?" said Daddy. "I am going to one of those windows to get tickets for our train ride. We cannot ride on the railroad without tickets."

Daddy went to a window and came back with four railroad tickets. "Now we'll go to the train," he said.

"You should get another ticket, Daddy," said Don. "Tad wants a ticket."

"Oh, no, a little boy like Tad can ride without a ticket," said Daddy.

They went down a long, long stairs and
came to the train. "Is the train waiting
for us?" asked Peggy.

"Yes, let's get on," said Daddy.

They went into one of the cars and sat
by some windows. Then the train started.
"Here we go," said Peggy.

Soon a trainman came through, calling,
"Tickets, please. Tickets, please."

Daddy got out his tickets and gave them
to the man. "Four tickets to Woodsfield,"
said the man, walking on.

Soon after the train left the station,
it went away from the big city. It went
from the city into the country.

On and on it went through the country.
It went by many farmhouses and barns,
and by farmers working in fields. It went
by cows eating grass in fields.

A farmer in a field waved at the train.
People on the train waved back at him
as they rode by. Don and Peggy waved,
and little Tad waved.

Now and then on the way the train ran
through small towns. Sometimes it came
to a stop in a small town.

By and by a trainman came into the car
and shouted, "Woodsfield is the next stop.
Out this way for Woodsfield."

"We are there!" cried the children.

The train came to a stop, and they went
from the car. The trainman helped them
to get off beside a small railroad station.
"Have a good time," he said.

"Hello, hello," called George and Teddy,
coming up with their father.

"Yes, hello there," called their father.
"We are happy to have you visit us. Now
let's go to the automobile."

Home on a Bus

On the way from the railroad station,
George said, "We are glad you could come.
We'll have a good visit."

"Yes, our fathers and mothers will have
a good visit, too," said Don.

The children found Lucky in the yard,
waiting for them. "Oh, look," cried Peggy.
"Here is Lucky."

"Bow-wow, bow-wow," went Lucky.

"He is happy to see you," said George.
"That is his way of telling you so."

"We want to show you our bunk beds,"
said Teddy. "George gets the high bunk
one week, and I the next."

They went upstairs to see the bunk beds.
As Tad looked at the high bunk, he said,
"Oh, my! What a place to sleep!"

"Let's go to see our school," said George.
"We like our school here."

They ran to see the Woodsfield school.
"What a pretty building!" said Peggy.

"Now let's play games with our friends,
Jack, Jean, and Linda," said Teddy. "Tad,
you may play with Timmie."

Don and Peggy had a good time, playing
games with Jack, Jean, and Linda. At last
Don said, "We have friends at Pine Square
with names just like yours."

Tad had fun playing with little Timmie.
"I like you, Timmie," he said. "You are
a little boy just like me."

A little while after dinner Daddy said,
"Well, it's time to start back to the city.
It's almost time for our bus."

"Are we going on a bus?" asked Don.

"Yes, there is no train back tonight,
so we'll go on a bus," said Daddy.

Soon they went to a small bus station,
and Daddy got four bus tickets. He got
no ticket for Tad.

"Tad is lucky," said Don. "He can ride
places without a ticket."

A big, wide bus came to the station.
Daddy gave his tickets to the bus man,
and they climbed inside.

"Good-by; good-by," everyone shouted
as the big, wide bus pulled away.

The bus went out into the country and
rolled along a country road to the city.
It was night, but the children could see
many things along the road.

"Oh, how pretty the sky looks tonight,"
said Peggy. "It's fun to watch the sky
from the bus window."

The people in the bus had a good time
talking and laughing. Some of them sang
songs. They sang old songs and new songs
over and over again.

Don and Peggy talked with a little girl,
and Tad soon went to sleep. "He has had
a big day," said Mother.

By and by they came to a bus station
in the city. "Come, children," said Daddy.
"We are back in the big city."

"Let me sleep," said Tad. "I want you
to carry me home."

Daddy had to carry Tad from the bus.

It's Fun to Ride a Bus

Oh, it's fun to ride a big, wide bus
　　Through rolling countryside.
It's fun to have the bus run on
　　While I just watch and ride.

It's fun to go from town to town
　　And see the things near by.
It's fun to look at farms and trees
　　And high up at the sky.

It's fun to watch the man up front
　　Who drives the bus along.
It's fun to hear the turning wheels
　　Make merry, merry song.

Yes, it's fun to ride a big, wide bus
　　Through rolling countryside.
It's fun to have the bus run on
　　While I just watch and ride.

Visiting the Water Front

The children at school were very happy. They were ready to go with Miss Jones to visit the water front.

"I know what the water front is like," said Don. "It is a place here in the city where streets meet the water."

"There are boats at the water front," said Peter. "We shall see many kinds of boats at the water front."

They went from the school building and
started down the street. Soon they came
to a traffic light on a corner. Mack said,
"We must watch the traffic light."

"Yes," said Peter. "We must wait here.
The traffic light is red."

Automobiles went by, one after another.
A truck came along and then a big bus.
Everyone watched and waited.

Soon the traffic light turned to green.
"Now we can go," said Miss Jones.

"The traffic lights help us to go places
in the city," said Jean. "What a time
we would have without them!"

By and by they came to some old houses along the street. "These old houses look like storybook houses," said Ann.

"Once Gingerbread Boy may have lived here," said Mack. "He may have run away from one of these houses."

All the children laughed.

"Some houses have fences," said Jack. "Maybe the woman lived here who went to market for a pig."

"Yes, maybe the stick began to beat the dog here, and the dog began to bite the pig," said Don.

All the children laughed again.

On and on they went. At all the corners they watched for traffic lights. They went only when the lights were green.

Near the water front a man walked out and held up his hand to stop the traffic. Then a railroad engine came along, pulling a train of cars.

The engine came to a stop and blocked the street. A man on the engine waved, and the children waved back.

"Some day I want to drive a big engine like that," said George.

"Why is the engine here?" asked Don.

"The railroad and boats work together," said Miss Jones. "Some of the cars bring loads to put on the boats. Others come to get loads from the boats."

Choo! Choo! The big engine moved on with its train of cars. "Come, let's look at the water front," said Miss Jones.

There were many boats on the water, big boats and little boats. Men worked to put loads on some of the big boats, and to take loads off other boats.

An old sailor came from a boat near by and walked along the water front. When he saw all the children he said, "Hello, little sailors, who are you?"

"Oh, we are not sailors," said Don. "We just came to see the boats."

"What do you think of that big, gray boat in front of you?" asked the sailor. "I work on that boat."

"We like the big, gray boat," said Peter. "What fun you must have going far away on that big boat."

"Yes, I have fun," said the sailor.

"Mr. Sailor, can you show us something from far away?" asked Jean.

The sailor began to think. Then he said, "Wait for me. I'll go on the boat to get something from far away."

The sailor went on his boat and brought back a little basket of stones. "Look here," he said. "Let me give you these stones. They came from far, far away."

"Thank you, but why do you bring stones in your boat?" said the children. "We have many stones here."

"Stones are very heavy," said the sailor. "All big boats need heavy things low down to help them go through the water."

"Tell us why they need heavy things low down," said the children.

The old sailor looked over at Miss Jones and smiled. "That is something to find out when you go back to school," he said. "Look in some of your books."

Miss Jones and the children went back to school. "Come, let's look," said Don. "We want to find out why big boats need heavy things low down."

The children looked to find out why
big boats need heavy things low down.
When the time came for them to go home,
they had not found out.

The next morning Peter said, "I know
why big boats need heavy things low down.
They need the heavy things to keep them
from rolling over."

"Good for you!" said Miss Jones. "Now
you know why the old sailor had stones
from far away on his boat."

Mike Takes a Sky Ride

One day at school the children talked about airplanes. Peter said, "One time I heard a funny story about an airplane. It took a tractor for a sky ride."

All the children said, "We want to hear tho story Please tell about the airplane that took a tractor for a sky ride. Where did it take the tractor?"

Then Peter began his story.

Once a farmer had a pretty red tractor that did many kinds of work on his farm. He called the red tractor Mike.

Mike liked to live and work on the farm. Day after day he went from field to field, pulling things for the farmer.

By and by the farmer moved to the city and had to sell Mike. From that time on, Mike worked at a big airfield. He pulled airplanes around the airfield.

Almost every day men started his engine and hitched him to big airplanes. Then he pulled the airplanes to the runway, where they could take off.

Mike looked very small as he pulled the airplanes with their big, wide wings. He looked almost like a toy.

One morning the men left Mike hitched to an airplane on the runway. They forgot to drive him away.

"I am afraid, hitched to this airplane," he said, starting to speak. "I am afraid that the airplane will start."

People came out to get on the airplane. Soon it was loaded, ready to take off, but no one came to get Mike. There he was, hitched to the airplane.

"How I wish that someone would come to get me," he said, speaking again. "I am afraid, hitched here as I am."

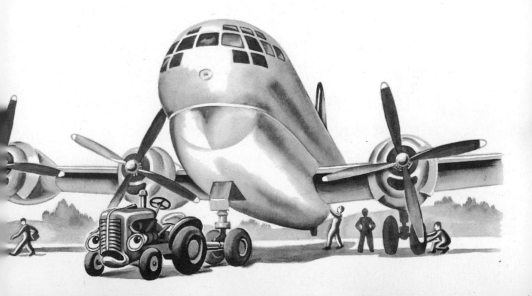

The big engines in the airplane went, "Zoom-m, zoom-m." The airplane started to move down the long runway. It pulled Mike down the runway after it.

Faster and faster went the big airplane, and after it went Mike, faster and faster. "Oh, please let me go," he called out, but the airplane only went faster.

Up from the airfield went the airplane, and up, too, went Mike. Soon he was flying in rain clouds high in the sky. They were so black that he could not see.

At first he was afraid up in the clouds, but he soon started to have fun. "I like to fly through rain clouds up in the sky," he said. "Now I am not afraid."

On and on he went through the clouds, high in the sky. He went from one cloud to another. He could not see a thing, but he was not afraid.

High in a cloud, the airplane went on
and left him. "What can I do?" he cried.
"I am not hitched to the airplane, and
I cannot fly without it."

Again he was afraid. He started to go
down faster and faster from the cloud.
"I'll crash when I come to the ground,"
he said on the way.

Faster and faster he went. He waited
to crash on the ground. Then suddenly
he came to a stop in a big stack of hay.
He did not crash on the ground at all,
and he was not hurt.

A farm boy saw Mike in the haystack
and called to his father. "Look, Daddy,"
he shouted. "See the pretty red tractor
in our haystack!"

The farmer ran to look at Mike. There
he was, a pretty red tractor in the stack
of hay, ready to work.

"What a big surprise!" said the farmer.
"Just when we need a tractor, we find one
here in our haystack."

"Yes, let's start his engine and put him
to work," said the boy.

Mike was happy as he began to work
on the farm. He had a good home again.

Mr. Jones and His Truck

The children were talking about trucks at school. By and by Jack said, "Let's tell stories about trucks. We can have fun telling truck stories."

The other children said, "Yes, let's tell truck stories. You tell a story first."

Then Jack made a picture of a truck, and started to tell his story.

Mr. Jones had a small trailer truck. The trailer looked like an old yellow box on wheels back of the engine.

Every day Mr. Jones made trips to move things about the city. He loaded things on his truck at one building and took them to another.

Almost every week Mr. Jones washed his trailer truck. He washed it to make it look pretty for his trips around the city. "It must look pretty," he said.

One day after washing his truck, he went
to a big building to get a load of groceries.
When he got there, he found men loading
packages on another trailer truck.

"Why are you men loading the packages
on that trailer truck?" he asked.

"Your trailer truck is too small to take
all the packages on one trip," they said.

Two men jumped on the big trailer truck
and went on their way with the heavy load.
They had to make a trip to the other side
of a wide river. Soon they came to a bridge
that went over the river.

"You cannot drive that big trailer truck
over this bridge," called out a policeman.
"It is too heavy for traffic here."

They went from this bridge to another.
Again a policeman said, "You cannot drive
that big trailer truck over this bridge.
It is too heavy for traffic here."

They found another bridge up the river. Once more a policeman came out to keep them off the bridge. "You cannot drive that big truck over this bridge," he said. "It is too heavy for traffic here."

"What shall we do?" asked the two men. "We must cross the river with this load of groceries somehow."

"Drive your truck to the river front," said the policeman. "You will find a boat there that takes trucks and automobiles across the river. Maybe you can cross the river on that boat."

The men went down to the river front
with their trailer truck. "You cannot put
that big truck on this boat," called a man.
"It is too heavy for boat traffic."

"Now what shall we do?" one man asked
the other on the truck.

"Let's just take the packages back where
we got them," said the other man.

Away they went back to the big building
to take the packages off their heavy truck.
Just then Mr. Jones came by the building
and began to laugh.

"My good little truck can cross the river
on the bridges and on the boat," he said.
"It is not too heavy for traffic."

Men came and began to put the packages
on Mr. Jones's trailer truck. They put on
all the packages that they could.

Then Mr. Jones jumped on his truck and
rode off to a bridge. The policeman waved
at him, and he went on across.

Soon he came back to get another load
of groceries. He made three trips to take
all the packages across the river.

"Other men may have their big trucks,"
he said with a smile. "As for me, I want
a truck that can go places."

Over the Countryside

A Surprise Telephone Call

One morning Ann had a telephone call from her friend Susan Stone. Susan lived in the country.

"Hello," said Susan on the telephone. "Do you know who I am?"

"Yes, I know who you are," said Ann. "You are Susan, but why do you call me on the telephone?"

"I am calling to ask you to come out for a visit," said Susan.

"What a surprise!" said Ann.

"I wanted to surprise you," said Susan. "That is why I called you by telephone, but will you come?"

"I'll have to ask my mother," said Ann. "She is out in the kitchen. Do not leave the telephone."

Ann ran to her mother in the kitchen. "Oh, Mother," she said. "Susan is calling on the telephone. She wants me to come for a visit. May I go?"

"Yes, Ann, you will have fun on a trip to the country," said her mother. "Tell Susan that you will come."

Ann went back to the telephone. "Yes, Susan, I'll come," she said.

"When will you come?" asked Susan. "Will you come tomorrow?"

"I forgot to ask," said Ann. "Let me go to talk with Mother again. Do not leave the telephone while I am away."

Ann ran to the kitchen. "Susan wants to know when to look for me," she said. "May I go tomorrow?"

"No, not tomorrow, but next Monday," answered her mother.

Ann ran back to the telephone. "Look for me next Monday," she said.

"We'll see you Monday," said Susan. "How will you come?"

"I forgot to ask," said Ann. "Let me go to talk with Mother again. Do not leave the telephone while I am away."

Ann ran back to the kitchen and said,
"Now Susan wants to know how I'll come.
What shall I tell her?"

"Tell her that you will come on a bus,"
answered her mother. "Ask her to have
someone meet you at the station."

Ann went back to the telephone again.
"I'll come on a bus, but I want someone
to meet me," she said.

"We'll meet you, but what time of day
will you leave?" asked Susan. "What bus
shall we meet?"

"Oh, my!" answered Ann. "I don't know.
Again I'll have to ask Mother."

Susan laughed and said, "What a time you and I have talking on the telephone! Every time I ask something, you run away to talk with your mother."

"Yes, I don't know how to answer you," said Ann. "Why not let my mother come to speak in my place?"

"I know," said Susan. "Let your mother speak with my mother."

The girls called their mothers to talk about Ann's trip. "She will come at three on Monday," said Ann's mother.

"We'll meet her at the bus station," said Susan's mother.

Two Girls on a Farm

On Monday Susan and her mother came to meet Ann at the bus station. "Hello," called Susan. "Here we are to meet you. Did you have a good trip?"

"Oh, yes, I had a good trip, thank you," said Ann. "It was fun to come out here on the big bus."

"Let me have your bag," said Susan.

The two girls climbed in the automobile with Susan's mother. Then they started off on a country road to the farm.

"Where is your father today?" Ann said to Susan on the way home.

"He is plowing corn today," said Susan. "He started to plow early this morning, and he has plowed all day."

"Is he working with his horses hitched to a plow?" asked Ann.

"No, he is working with his tractor," said Susan. "When we get home, we'll go to the cornfield to see him."

"While you girls run to the cornfield, I'll make a cake," said Mrs. Stone. "How would you like a cake for dinner?"

"Oh, a cake will be good for dinner," said the girls.

When they got home, the girls put on old clothes and started to the cornfield. Mrs. Stone began to make a cake.

"Don't miss dinner," she said. "Hurry back to get the good cake."

As the girls walked along, they came
to some cows looking through a fence.
"These are our cows," said Susan.

They looked at the cows for a while
and then walked on to the big cornfield.
There they found Mr. Stone on his way
across the field with his tractor.

"What a loud noise the tractor makes!"
said Ann. "Hear it go huff, huff, huff, and
puff, puff, puff, pulling the plow."

"Yes, the tractor makes a loud noise
pulling the plow," said Susan. "It keeps
going huff, huff, huff, and puff, puff, puff
as it plows the corn."

After the girls watched Mr. Stone plow
his corn, they began to look for flowers.
Soon they came to a woods.

They found pretty flowers in the woods,
and started to pick some to take with them.
"These flowers will be pretty on the table
with Mother's cake," said Susan.

Next the girls sat down on the ground
to talk. While they talked, they could hear
the loud noise of Mr. Stone's big tractor.
"Your father keeps plowing and plowing
all the time," said Ann.

Before long they missed the huff, huff
and the puff, puff of Mr. Stone's tractor.
"He is not plowing," said Ann.

"No, let's go to see why," said Susan.
"Why did he stop?"

Just then they heard him start to shout,
"Get out! Get out of the corn."

"The cows are in the corn," cried Susan.
"Let's run to help drive them out before
they hurt the corn."

"How will they hurt the corn?" said Ann.
"What will they do to it?"

"Oh, they will eat it, and beat it down
with their feet," said Susan.

The girls ran fast to help Mr. Stone
drive the cows out of the cornfield. As
they ran, they could hear him shouting,
"Get out! Get out of the corn."

"Here we are, Father," called Susan.
"We'll help to drive them out."

The big old cows ran this way and that before Mr. Stone and the girls. At last they went through the hole in the fence where they had come in.

Mr. Stone blocked the hole in the fence to keep the cows from coming in again. "Now the big cows cannot eat your corn," said Ann, watching. "They cannot beat it down with their feet."

"I am glad that we got them out today when we did," said Mr. Stone.

"We are glad, too," said the girls.

The Baby Ducks

Susan and Ann came to eat breakfast
in the kitchen. While they were eating,
Susan said, "I have some ducks for pets.
I have some baby ducks."

"Good!" said Ann. "Where did you get
your pet ducks?"

"From some duck eggs," answered Susan.
"Mother let me have some duck eggs, and
I put them under an old chicken hen. Now
the old hen has baby ducks."

Ann laughed and laughed. "How funny!" she said. "The old chicken hen has ducks. Does she like her baby ducks?"

"Oh, yes, but she thinks that they are chickens," said Susan. "She does not know that they are ducks."

"She does not know now, but some day she will know," said Ann.

"She will know when the ducks get big," said Susan.

Susan got out bread for the mother hen and baby ducks. "They like to eat bread," she said. "I feed them bread every day, and other things, too."

"Feed the little chickens this morning," said Mrs. Stone. "Take some bread along for them when you go."

Susan got bread for the little chickens. "Come, Ann," she said. "We are ready to feed the ducks and chickens."

"Let's feed the ducks first," said Ann.
"I want to see the baby ducks."

"Look at that small box with a door
at the front," said Susan. "That is where
I keep the old hen and baby ducks. I put
them inside every night and let them out
every morning."

The girls ran to the box. "Oh, look!"
called Susan. "The old hen is not here,
and my baby ducks are not here. I forgot
to put them in last night. Let's hurry
to tell Mother about them."

"Mother, oh, Mother," shouted Susan on the run. "My hen and ducks are gone. Where can they be?"

"I don't know," said Mrs. Stone. "Look in the barn and fields. You may find them somewhere on the farm."

"Let's look," said Susan.

The girls looked for the hen and ducks. They looked in the barn and in the fields, but could not find them. "We have gone all over the farm," said Susan. "Come, let's go back to the house."

On the way the girls crossed a bridge. "Look, Susan, look," cried Ann. "There are some ducks on the water."

Susan ran over to the side of the bridge to look. "Those are my ducks," she cried. "At last we have found them."

"See the old hen," said Ann. "She wants the baby ducks to come out of the water, but does not know what to do. Look at her wave her feet and wings."

"Yes, the old hen is finding out that her chickens are ducks," said Susan.

Then the girls laughed and laughed.

Susan and Her Garden

"How would you like to see my garden?" asked Susan.

"Oh, a garden!" said Ann. "Have you a garden this summer?"

"Yes, I have a good one," said Susan. "Every summer I put out a garden here on the farm."

"How I wish that I could have a garden in summer," said Ann. "In the big city I have no room for one."

The two girls ran out to the big garden on the farm. "My little garden is a part of the big garden," said Susan. "Come this way to see it."

"Your garden has two parts," said Ann. "You have one part for your vegetables and one part for your flowers."

"Yes, I have one part for vegetables and another part for flowers," said Susan. "I like to keep all my vegetables together and all my flowers together."

"What do you do with your vegetables after you pick them?" asked Ann. "What do you do with your flowers?"

"I sell most of them to people in town," said Susan. "In that way I make money. When the summer is over, I hope to have money for a new doll and doll cart."

"Just think!" said Ann. "You will have a new doll and doll cart."

The girls looked first at the flowers
in the garden, and then at the vegetables.
"Here are some vegetables ready to sell,"
said Susan. "Let's pick them and get them
ready for market."

Susan ran to the house and came back
with a basket. Then she and Ann began
to pick vegetables.

"This is fun," cried Ann. "I never did
this work before. I never helped to pick
things from a garden."

"Yes, every summer I have fun picking
things from my garden," said Susan.

148

Susan's mother got out the automobile to take the girls into town. "Let's drive on Water Street when we come to town," said Susan. "The people there like to get vegetables from me."

Mrs. Stone turned off on Water Street and came to a stop. Then Susan got out with her basket of vegetables. "Please come with me to help sell the vegetables," she said to Ann.

Away the two girls started, carrying the basket of vegetables.

Soon they saw an old woman in her yard. "There is poor Mrs. Woods, who never has any money," said Susan.

"See the poor old woman look and look," said Ann. "She looks as if she wants some of your vegetables."

"Yes, but she has no money," said Susan. "I must find people with money."

"Then how will the poor old woman get any vegetables?" asked Ann. "She wants to eat, just as other people do."

"Oh, my!" cried Susan. "I did not think of that. I was only thinking of the money that I would get."

"Well, let's go on," said Ann. "Let's find some people with money."

"No, I don't want to go on," said Susan. "I'll let Mrs. Woods have my vegetables today. I don't need the money as much as she needs the vegetables."

The girls went over to the poor woman.
"Hello, Mrs. Woods," called Susan. "How
would you like to have some vegetables?
I brought them from my garden."

"Oh, I should like them, but I don't have
any money," answered Mrs. Woods.

"You don't need any money," said Susan.
"I want to give them to you."

"Thank you," said Mrs. Woods. "You are
a good little girl."

Soon the girls were in the automobile
on their way home. "I never saw anyone
so glad as Mrs. Woods," said Susan.

A Garden for Me

I have a little garden
   That I made just for me.
It's a small kind of garden,
   But, oh, so good to see!

My daddy plants a garden
   And works there day by day.
I plant a better garden,
   My daddy likes to say.

It's a good spot to work, and
   It's a good spot to play.
Oh, how I like to go there
   On any summer day.

What Visits the Garden?

"Come, let's look at my garden again,"
said Susan one morning. "Maybe we'll find
more vegetables ready for market. Then
we shall have work to do."

The girls ran to the garden. Suddenly
Susan came to a stop. "Oh, my!" she said.
"Something has been in my garden. Look
at these plants."

"Yes, parts of the plants are gone,"
said Ann. "Something has been eating
the leaves of the plants."

"Let's get Mother," said Susan.

The girls ran to get Mrs. Stone. "Come, see the plants in my garden," said Susan. "Something has been eating them."

Mrs. Stone went to the garden. "Yes, something has been eating your plants," she said. "Parts of them are gone."

"What was it, Mother?" asked Susan. "Was it a squirrel?"

"Not a squirrel," laughed Mrs. Stone. "It must have been a rabbit."

"The rabbit ate parts of my poor plants, and I don't want it in here," said Susan. "How did it get into the garden?"

"I don't know, but you might find out by watching," said Mrs. Stone. "Be quiet, and the rabbit might come back."

"Yes, it might come back," said Susan. "We might see how it got in."

The two girls sat down near the garden to watch. They were quiet, as quiet as they could be. All day they watched, but the rabbit did not come back.

"We might as well give up," said Susan. "The rabbit is not coming today."

The next morning the girls woke up early and ran out to look at the plants. "More leaves are gone," said Susan.

"Yes, the rabbit has been here again," said Ann. "It came back at night when everything was quiet."

The girls started to leave. On the way
Ann looked through the fence into a field.
Suddenly she said, "Oh, look, Susan! See
those little pieces over there on the grass.
They look like pieces of fur."

"Let's find out," said Susan.

They ran from the garden to the field
to look at the little pieces on the grass.
"Yes, they are pieces of fur," said Susan.
"They are pieces of rabbit fur."

"Look under the grass," said Ann. "See
the hole in the ground. There are pieces
of fur all around the hole."

"Let's move the grass so that we can see the hole better," said Susan.

When they moved the grass and looked at the hole, they saw more pieces of fur. "These pieces of fur make the hole look like a nest," said Ann.

They got down to look inside the hole. "Yes, it's a nest," cried Susan. "There are bunny rabbits here."

She took out four bunny rabbits and put them on the ground. They were so small that they could not see or walk.

The two girls ran fast to tell Mrs. Stone about the little rabbits. "Come, Mother," cried Susan. "We have found a rabbit nest with four bunny rabbits."

Mrs. Stone went with the girls to see the bunny rabbits. "How small they are!" she said. "Let's put them inside the nest where they belong."

They put the rabbits back in the hole with pieces of fur around them. They put the grass back, just as it had been before. "We must not let the mother rabbit know that we were here," said Mrs. Stone.

"Where did she get fur to make a nest for her rabbits?" asked Ann.

"She pulled off pieces of her own fur to make it," said Mrs. Stone. "She made it out of her own fur."

"She made a good nest for the rabbits out of her own fur," said Ann.

"How strange that we never have seen the old mother rabbit," said Susan.

"Oh, she does not want you to see her," said Mrs. Stone. "She comes at night when things are quiet."

That night the girls went out to watch for the mother rabbit. By and by they saw her come to visit her little baby rabbits. Then she came on to the garden.

"Oh, look!" said Ann. "There she comes under the garden fence."

"She comes in as if the vegetables were her own," said Susan. "We'll have to put something by the fence to keep her out. She must eat in the fields."

Blue Mr. Blue

The day's work was over on the farm, and everyone sat down to talk for a while. "I hear that Mr. Blue hurt his leg today," said Mr. Stone.

"Does he need help?" asked Mrs. Stone. "Who will do his work?"

"I don't know," said Mr. Stone. "He has no telephone, so we cannot talk with him. Tomorrow I'll go over to see."

"Yes, you know that he never would ask for help," said Mrs. Stone.

That night after the girls went to bed, Ann said, "Who is Mr. Blue?"

"He is an old man who lives near here on a little farm," said Susan. "He lives all alone in his house."

"He must be very sad to live all alone in his house," said Ann. "He does not have anyone to make him happy."

"He does not want anyone to make him happy," said Susan. "He wants to be sad, and he wants to be alone. People call him blue Mr. Blue."

"Has he any friends?" asked Ann.

"Not that I know of," answered Susan. "He talks with people only now and then, and never visits them."

"He must be a strange man," said Ann. "I wish that I could see him."

"We might go along with Father to see him tomorrow," said Susan.

The next morning Susan and Ann went
with Mr. Stone to see old Mr. Blue. When
they walked up to the house, they knocked
on the door. Then they heard someone say,
"Please come in."

They went into the house. Mr. Blue sat
in a chair with one leg on another chair.
"Good morning," he said.

"You hurt your leg," said Mr. Stone.

"Yes, I am a sad old man all alone here
this morning," said Mr. Blue.

"We came to help you," said Mr. Stone.

"Oh, good!" said Mr. Blue. "Please look
after my chickens and pigs."

Mr. Stone and the two girls started out to feed the chickens and pigs. All at once Mr. Blue said, "Why not let the girls stay in the house, Mr. Stone? I don't want to be alone this morning."

"Poor Mr. Blue," said Susan. "Let's play that you are Grandfather."

"Yes, just play that I am Grandfather," said Mr. Blue with a smile. "From now on, call me Grandfather Blue."

"That will be fun, Grandfather Blue," said Ann. "We can have a very good time, staying here with you."

Mr. Stone went on out of the house, and the two girls stayed inside with Mr. Blue. "We are surprised that you want us to call you Grandfather," said Susan.

"Why so?" asked Mr. Blue. "It makes me very happy for you to call me Grandfather. It keeps me from being sad."

"How strange!" said Susan. "People say that you want to be sad and stay here alone. They say that you do not want to be happy like other people."

"People just do not know me very well," said Mr. Blue, starting to laugh a little. "I want to be happy, but I have no one to make me happy."

"Then let us make you happy," said Ann. "We are going to call you Grandfather and make you very happy."

Mr. Blue laughed, and the girls laughed. They started to have a good time.

"Now, Grandfather Blue," said the girls.
"May we get you something to eat?"

"Yes, thank you," he said.

They brought apples, cookies, and milk
from Mr. Blue's kitchen. "Get some chairs
and eat with me," he said.

"This is like a party," said Ann.

"How strange!" said Mr. Blue, looking
at his leg. "I had to hurt my leg to get you
to come to visit me."

Everyone looked at his leg on the chair
and suddenly began to laugh. "We like
you, Grandfather Blue," said the girls.

The Proud Cow

After dinner Susan and Ann sat down
to read books. Susan began to read stories
about farm animals, and Ann began to read
stories about circus animals.

By and by Susan looked up and said,
"This book has good stories and pictures.
Here is a good story about a proud cow,
and here is her picture."

"I want to hear the story," said Ann.
"Please read it to me."

Then Susan began to read Ann a story
about a proud cow.

Once upon a time a farmer had a cow
that gave very good milk. Often he said
to her, "You are a grand cow. You give
the best milk in all the land."

The cow liked to hear the farmer say
that she was grand. She liked to hear
him say that she gave the best milk
in all the land.

By and by the cow became very proud.
Day after day she said around the farm,

"I am a proud cow
And very grand.
My milk is the best
In all the land."

After a while the cow became too proud
for the farm. "This farm is a poor place
for a good cow like me," she said. "I give
the best milk in all the land."

One summer day she ran away to tell
everyone how very grand she was.

Soon the cow wanted a drink of water.
She went to a river and said, "Oh, river,
give me a drink of water."

"What will you give me for the water?"
asked the river.

Then the cow said,

> "I am a proud cow
> And very grand.
> My milk is the best
> In all the land."

"What is that to me?" asked the river.
"I don't drink milk, so you cannot have
any water. Leave me alone."

The cow wanted a bite of grass to eat.
She went to a field and said, "Oh, field,
give me a bite of grass to eat."

"What will you give me for the grass?"
asked the field.

Then the cow said,

> "I am a proud cow
> And very grand.
> My milk is the best
> In all the land."

"What is that to me?" asked the field,
"I don't drink milk, so you cannot have
a bite of grass. Leave me alone."

The proud cow went away.

Everywhere the cow went in the country,
she was turned down. No one at all wanted
to have anything to do with her. She might
be very grand, but what of that?

"I might as well go back to the farm,"
she cried. "On the farm I can get water
to drink and grass to eat."

She turned about and started back home
to the farm. When she came to the barn
once more, she said,

"If I can walk through this door,

I'll never be proud any more."

The old farmer saw the cow and ran fast
to let her inside. He opened the barn door,
and in she went on the run.

"How glad I am to see you!" he called
as he ran after her. "I have been watching
and waiting for you to come back to me.
Let me give you some good water to drink
and good grass to eat."

Once more the farmer looked at the cow and said, "You are a grand cow. You give the best milk in all the land."

"Don't call me grand," said the cow. "I ran away from your farm because I was proud, but I am not proud any more."

"You give the best milk in all the land," said the farmer. "There is no other cow like you in all the land."

"I am the best cow only because you are the best farmer," said the cow.

From then on the cow was very happy, but she never was proud again.

Peter's One Big Wish

The next night after dinner Ann asked, "Shall we read this evening? Shall we read stories again?"

"We might hear a good story on the radio this evening," answered Susan. "It's time for Uncle Tom to tell a story."

"Oh, yes, let's hear a story on the radio this evening," said Ann.

The girls ran to turn on the radio. Soon they heard Uncle Tom say, "Good evening, boys and girls. This is your radio friend Uncle Tom. Here I am to tell you a story about a little pumpkin called Peter."

Peter Pumpkin lived in a big cornfield on a farm. Like most pumpkins, he wanted to become big, but he never did. He stayed little all summer long.

When summer was over, a farmer came to pick pumpkins. He looked down at Peter and said, "This pumpkin is not big enough. He looks like a little balloon."

The farmer left Peter right where he was on the ground. Peter was very sad because the farmer left him there.

"Oh, my," said Peter. "The farmer says that I am not big enough. He thinks that I look like a little balloon."

Then Peter cried and cried.

"I want to become a pumpkin pie, as all pumpkins do," said Peter. "I may be as small as a balloon, but I know that I am big enough for a pie."

He saw his old friend, Mr. Blackwing, and said, "I am very sad here all alone. The farmer does not want me for a pie because I am not big enough. He thinks that I look like a little balloon."

"It is not right," said Mr. Blackwing. "No, it is not right, but don't give up hope. One of these days, friend Peter, someone will want you."

"Thank you, kind Mr. Blackwing," said Peter. "I shall not give up hope."

Before many days, the farmer brought his little girl to the field. "Oh, Father, see this little pumpkin," she said.

"Yes, he looks like a little balloon," said the farmer. "I left him here because he is not big enough for a pie."

"He is big enough for a pie for me," said the girl. "It would be fun to have a little pie all my own."

Peter heard what the little girl said, and it made him very, very glad. At last someone wanted him, and he was going to become a pie.

The girl picked him and started away to the house. "Oh, Mother," she called. "See this little pumpkin. Please make him into a pie all my own."

The girl watched her mother make Peter into a little pie. "What a good pie for a little girl," said her mother.

At last Peter had his wish. He was just
a little pumpkin pie, but that was what
he wanted to become.

"Uncle Tom had a very good story for us
this evening," said Ann. "When I go back
to the city, I want to hear Uncle Tom tell
stories on our radio."

"You will like his stories," said Susan.
"He tells a good one every evening. When
I come to visit you sometime, we'll hear
him together on your radio."

In Storyland –
New Stories

The Funny Old Clock

Once there was an old house. At first no one lived in the house. Then by and by an old woman came to live there.

The old woman found an old, old clock in the house. "Look, old clock," she said. "This house is far too quiet, and I want a little noise here. Why don't you say ticktock for me?"

"No," said the clock. "I must laugh before I can say ticktock."

The old woman went to a fireplace and
made a fire. Before long the fire began
to go crackle and snap, crackle and snap
in the fireplace.

"What a good fire!" said the old woman.
"The fire burns and burns for me. Hear
it go crackle and snap, crackle and snap
in the old fireplace."

The fire burned on and made more noise.
"Now the house is not too quiet for me,"
smiled the old woman.

By and by she looked at the old clock.
"This good fire should please the clock,"
she said. "It might make the clock laugh.
Then it would say ticktock."

She went over to the clock and said,
"Hear the good fire go crackle and snap.
Now won't you say ticktock for me?"

"No," said the clock. "I cannot laugh,
so I cannot say ticktock."

"There is no way to help one's self with that clock," said the old woman. "What shall I do?"

She sat down in a chair by the fire. Soon the chair began to go crickety-crick, crickety-crick, crickety-crick. Once more the fire began to go crackle and snap, crackle and snap, crackle and snap.

Again the old woman said to the clock, "Won't you say ticktock for me?"

"No," said the clock. "I cannot laugh, so I cannot say ticktock."

The old woman said to herself, "What shall I do now?"

She put a kettle of water over the fire in the fireplace. Soon the kettle started to go ah-mm, ah-mm. Again the fire went crackle and snap, crackle and snap. And once more the chair went crickety-crick, crickety-crick.

The old woman went over to the clock and said, "Hear all these loud noises. Now won't you say ticktock for me?"

"No," said the clock. "I cannot laugh, so I cannot say ticktock."

"The clock does not want to say ticktock any more," said the old woman to herself. "I might as well give up."

That evening a kitten came to the door. "Mew, mew! Mew, mew!" she cried.

The old woman heard the kitten mewing, and got her some milk to drink. After that the kitten went to sleep.

Suddenly all the noises started again. Once more the fire in the fireplace began to go crackle and snap, crackle and snap. Then the chair began to go crickety-crick, crickety-crick. The kettle of water began to go ah-mm, ah-mm.

The noises woke the kitten. She jumped up on a chair and began to go fst, fst, fst at the old woman.

The clock looked down at the kitten and started to smile. Then it began to laugh, "Ha, ha," and "Ha, ha, ha."

The old woman looked up at the clock in surprise. "Why, you laughed!" she said. "Now you can say ticktock."

"Yes, ticktock, ticktock," said the clock. "Ticktock, ticktock, ha, ha, ha."

Then crackle and snap, crackle and snap started the fire once more. Crickety-crick, crickety-crick started the chair once again. Ah-mm, ah-mm went the kettle.

With all these noises the old woman was very, very happy. Her house was not quiet, and the clock said ticktock.

The Birds' Singing Party

Long, long ago the birds of the woods had
a singing party. They wanted to find out
who could sing the best song.

They had a good prize for the best song.
The prize was a stone bath under a tree
in the woods. All the birds wanted to get
the stone bath for a prize.

In those days birds sang from songbooks.
They sang out of books for the squirrels
and other animals in the woods. They had
to read all their songs.

One bird who was to sing at the party
had a long tail. The other birds called
him old Mr. Long-Tail.

When he started to get his song ready,
he could not find his songbook. Where
could it be? He asked Mrs. Long-Tail,
but she did not know.

"You must find your songbook because
we need a birdbath," she said. "I want
you to get the prize."

Mr. Long-Tail went to see Mr. Bluebird
about his songbook. "Chirp, chirp, chirp,
come in," said Mr. Bluebird.

"Chirp, chirp, chirp, yes, thank you,"
answered Mr. Long-Tail. "Have you seen
my little songbook? I have lost it, and
now I cannot read my song."

"No, I have not seen your songbook,
but here is my book," said Mr. Bluebird.
"You may read my book."

Mr. Long-Tail looked at the pretty song in Mr. Bluebird's book. "Please show me how it goes," he said.

Mr. Bluebird took the book and said, "I am very proud of my little song. It is a grand song, the best in all the woods. Here is how it goes."

He sang his song for Mr. Long-Tail, and then Mr. Long-Tail sang it back to him. "You see how my little song goes, and sing it very well," said Mr. Bluebird.

"Yes, I like your pretty little song and the way it goes," answered Mr. Long-Tail. "Thank you for singing it to me."

By and by Mr. Long-Tail went to see
Mr. Robin. "Chirp, chirp, have you seen
my little songbook?" he asked.

"No, I have not seen your songbook, but
you may look at my book," said Mr. Robin.
"Here is my book."

"Please show me how your song goes,"
said Mr. Long-Tail.

Mr. Robin sang his pretty little song,
and then Mr. Long-Tail sang it back to him.
"You see how my little song goes, and sing
it very well," said Mr. Robin.

"Yes, I like your pretty little song and
the way it goes," answered Mr. Long-Tail.
"Thank you for singing it to me."

Mr. Long-Tail went on from bird to bird
in the woods. He did not find his songbook,
but he heard all the songs in the woods.
He sang all the songs.

"Did you find your book while you were
away?" asked Mrs. Long-Tail.

"No, but I saw the other birds' books,"
said Mr. Long-Tail. "I sang every song
in the woods and know just how it goes.
I have lost my songbook, but I can mock
all the other birds."

At last came the day of the big party.
All the birds came out to sing their songs
for the squirrels and other animals. Soon
Mr. Long-Tail began to sing.

"That is my song!" said Mr. Bluebird.
"Hear him mock me as he sings."

"Now he mocks me," said Mr. Robin.

"He mocks all of us," said the others.
"He sings all our songs."

"Mr. Long-Tail should get the birdbath,"
said Mr. Gray Squirrel. "He mocked you,
but he sang your songs well."

"Yes, give Mr. Long-Tail the birdbath,"
said Mr. Red Squirrel.

The birds gave Mr. Long-Tail the prize.
He and Mrs. Long-Tail were very happy
with their new birdbath.

Mr. Bluebird said, "You mocked us today
with your song. From now on we are going
to call you Mr. Mocking Bird."

After that when a bird forgot his song,
he went to old Mr. Mocking Bird for help.
Mr. Mocking Bird never forgot a song.

An Elf Plays Tricks

Once Farmer Brown put up a new barn for his animals. He moved the animals from an old barn to the new one.

A little elf saw the new barn and said, "I'll move in, too. I can have fun playing tricks on the animals."

So the elf moved in. He began to hide here and there, where no one would look. "I do not want anyone to know that I am staying here," he said. "I'll just call myself Mr. Hide-Away."

Right away the elf began to play tricks on the animals. He got on their backs, and he climbed up their legs. He pulled their ears and tails.

One morning he scratched an old horse on its nose, and the old horse ran away. Then he scratched an old cow on its nose, and the old cow ran away. In a few days there were no animals left.

Farmer Brown was surprised. He said, "What happened to all my animals here in the new barn? In a few days they ran away and won't come back. I'll look about to see what I can find."

By and by when he went into the barn, something knocked off his hat. He picked it up, and something knocked it off again. "Strange things happen," he said.

Then the elf began to laugh, but not so the farmer could hear.

Some mice came to the barn and began to hide in the hay. Then an old cat came to catch the mice.

At once the elf began to play tricks on the cat. When she looked for the mice, he scratched her nose and pulled her ears. When she ran after the mice, he pulled her feet and legs.

"Something hides here besides mice," she said to herself.

One day she played that she was asleep in the barn. She saw the elf come near to scratch her nose. From that time on she wanted to catch the elf.

Farmer Brown happened to see the mice
in the barn. "There are mice here," he said.
"Now I know why the animals do not want
to stay in the barn."

He brought traps to the barn. He put
little traps all over the hay. "In a few days
I'll catch these mice," he said. "After that
the animals will come back."

"How happy I would be if he would catch
the old cat in a trap," said the elf. "I'll hide
here to watch."

"How I wish that he would catch the elf
in a trap," said the old cat.

The one wanted the other to get caught
in a trap for the mice.

That evening the elf called a few mice together. "Watch where you go," he said. "Farmer Brown has put traps in the hay to catch you."

Then he said, "The old cat is no friend of yours, for she wants to catch you, too. Let's all work together to get her caught in a trap."

"Oh, good!" cried the mice. "We'll work to get her caught."

When the cat saw what was happening, she said, "I must watch out. They want to play a trick on me."

The next morning Farmer Brown looked at his traps, but found no mice in them. "How strange!" he said. "There should be a few mice in the traps."

Suddenly off went his hat. Every time he put it on, down it went to the ground. "More strange things happen," he said.

All day the elf and the mice worked
to trick the old cat. "Come and get us,"
they said, but she would not come.

Then something happened. All at once
the elf began to roll fast down the hay.
He rolled faster and faster, and landed
right in a trap. "Help, help!" he called
to the mice.

The mice ran to help him, but were
too little to open the trap. They pulled
this way and that, but he was fast. How
would he ever get out? Who ever heard
of an elf in a trap?

The old cat laughed and laughed when she saw the poor elf in the trap. At last he could play no more tricks.

"Please help me," cried the elf.

"I'll help you only if you will be good," said the happy old cat. "You must play no more tricks."

"May I knock off Farmer Brown's hat once in a while?" asked the elf.

"Only on Saturdays," said the old cat, coming near the trap.

Then she let the elf out. From then on just one thing ever happened in the barn. Whenever Farmer Brown came in the door on Saturday, he had to pick up his hat.

The Surprised Peddler

Once a peddler walked around the city selling some caps. He did not keep his caps inside a bag, but had them in a high stack. He looked very, very funny walking along with his stack of caps.

People often laughed at the peddler as he went along with his caps. They liked to watch him because he was funny.

.Sometimes the peddler held the stack
of caps in his hands. Sometimes he put it
on his head. People laughed all the more
when he put it on his head.

First in his stack he had his own cap
of black and gray. Over this he had caps
of four colors to sell. He had green caps,
yellow caps, then blue caps. Last of all,
he had red caps.

"How can he keep them on his head?"
people said when they saw him. "Why
don't they ever roll off?"

But they never did.

One day the peddler went up the street with the stack of caps on his head. First, he had on his own cap of black and gray. Over this he had his caps of four colors, green, yellow, blue, and red.

As he walked up the street, he called, "Caps to sell," but no one wanted any of his caps. No one wanted a green cap. No one wanted a yellow cap, a blue cap, or a red cap.

The peddler walked on and on. At last he left the city and came to the country. He went along an old country road until he came to a tree. "Here is a good place to stop for a while," he said.

He sat down by the trunk of the tree with the stack of caps high on his head. "I'll sleep by the trunk of this old tree until evening," he said. "Then I'll go back to the city again."

After a long time the peddler woke up. He put his hand up to his head, and what a surprise! The only cap on his head was his own cap of black and gray. "Where are the other caps?" he said.

He looked all around the tree. He looked to the front of him and back of him. There were no caps to be seen.

"How strange!" he said. "When I came, I had green caps, yellow caps, blue caps, and red caps. Now all that I have left is my own cap of black and gray. I have no caps left to sell."

By and by he looked up into the tree, and what do you think he saw? There were monkeys in the tree, and every monkey had on a colored cap.

The peddler looked up at the monkeys and said, "Give me my caps."

The monkeys just started to mock him and said, "Tze, tze, tze."

He held up his hands to the monkeys and said, "Don't mock me. Let me have my caps to sell."

Then the monkeys held up their hands, just as the peddler did.

By this time the peddler was very cross.
He jumped up and down and said, "Give me
my caps, you old monkeys."

Then the monkeys jumped up and down,
just as the peddler did.

By and by the peddler became so cross
that he pulled off his cap. Down it rolled
to the ground! When this happened, what
do you think the monkeys did? They pulled
off their caps, too.

Then all the green caps,

and all the yellow caps,

and all the blue caps,

and all the red caps
came flying down to the ground.

The peddler put the caps on his head.
Over his own cap of black and gray he put
green caps, then yellow caps, blue caps,
and red caps. Back to the city he went,
calling, "Caps to sell."

The Eggs in Pretty Colors

All the eggs in Easter Land were glad because Easter was coming the next week. They were dressed in very pretty colors, waiting for Easter to come.

"I am proud of my color," said Red Egg. "Children like red eggs on Easter."

"My color is better," said Blue Egg. "Children like blue eggs better."

"My color is best," said Yellow Egg. "Children like yellow eggs best."

The proud little eggs talked on and on about their pretty colors.

One egg was pink, and called Pink Egg.
This egg was not proud and did not want
to talk about her color. She just wanted
to run and play.

By and by she climbed on a stone fence
to look around. "Tell us what you see,"
said the other eggs.

"All of Easter Land," said Pink Egg.
"Come up and see, too."

"Oh, no," said Red Egg. "We might fall
and hurt our colors."

"I am not afraid," laughed Pink Egg.

After Pink Egg had been on the fence for a while, she wanted to get down. Then suddenly she began to fall.

"Oh, look!" cried the other eggs. "See Pink Egg! See Pink Egg fall!"

After her fall, Pink Egg did not move. "Did I break my back?" she asked.

"Did little Pink Egg break her back?" asked all the other eggs. "Did she break her back? If she did, she won't be good for Easter next week."

"What shall we do?" asked Red Egg.

"Let's ask old Humpty Dumpty to come
and look at Pink Egg," said Yellow Egg.
"He should know about her back because
once he had a big fall."

"Yes, get old Humpty Dumpty to look
at Pink Egg," said Blue Egg. "Be quick!
Be quick! Be as quick as you can."

Off they ran to get old Humpty Dumpty.
All the while little Pink Egg was saying,
"I had a big fall. Did I break my back?
Did I break my back?"

The other eggs called, "Did she break
her back? Humpty Dumpty should know."

Humpty Dumpty came to the fence to see Pink Egg. He rolled her over and got down to look at her back.

"What do you think, Humpty Dumpty?" said all the eggs. "Did Pink Egg break her back?"

"I do not know," said Humpty Dumpty, looking very sad. "I cannot see as well as I did. My big fall hurt me, and I am not a good egg any more."

"Look at her again," said Yellow Egg. "Be quick, Humpty Dumpty. Did she break her back? If she did, she won't be good for Easter next week."

"Yes, every egg must have a good back for Easter," said Humpty Dumpty. Then he began to look at Pink Egg again. "What do you say?" cried the eggs.

"I cannot tell," said Humpty Dumpty. "Maybe Easter Bunny can tell."

Easter Bunny came to look at Pink Egg.
"What are you doing here?" he asked.

"I had a fall," answered Pink Egg.

"A fall!" said Easter Bunny. "Get up!
You did not break your back."

Little Pink Egg jumped up. "Oh, look!"
she said. "Why, I did not break my back.
I am just as good as I ever was."

After that Pink Egg did not climb again
all week. Then when Easter morning came,
she waited in a pretty basket by a house.
By and by some children came to get her,
and she made them very happy.

The Happy Little Broom

It was only a few days until Halloween.
Halloween pumpkins could be seen in some
of the windows.

An old peddler went down a country road
with his horse and wagon. He had brooms
to sell, all kinds of brooms, big and little.
People could get whatever kind of broom
they wanted.

By evening the peddler was ready to go
home. "I have only one little broom left
in my wagon," he said. "No one wants it,
so I'll burn it when I get home."

The little broom was very sad because he was going to be burned. "I don't want to be burned," he said. "If only I had wings, I would fly away."

Just then one of the wagon wheels went over a stone, and the broom rolled out. "Ha, ha," he laughed. "I'll hide myself in the grass until the peddler goes on. He won't ever see me again."

The little broom rolled into the grass and waited until the peddler was gone. When he got up, he saw a big farmhouse near by. "I'll go there," he said. "Maybe someone there will want me."

As he went along, he happened to think that Halloween was near. He would make a good broom for Halloween.

"All children like Halloween," he said. "I would make a good Halloween present for some boy or girl."

The little broom soon came to the house and found that it was very, very old. There were no people around, for no one lived there any more.

The door was open, so the broom went in and looked around. He walked along a hall with a few rooms at the side. "How quiet everything is," he said.

Suddenly he heard a noise in the hall, and there before him he saw a little witch. Coming along the hall was a big black cat with its long tail held up high. It looked like a Halloween cat.

The little witch and the black cat met
in the hall and began to talk together.
What a strange pair they made!

"They look like a pair that have met
here to make up tricks," said the broom.
"I'll hide in a room off the hall to hear
what they talk about."

"I have no broomstick for Halloween,"
the little witch started to say. "I need
one to ride through the sky."

"Yes, you need a broomstick to ride
on Halloween," said the cat.

"Why, I would make a nice broomstick for the witch," the broom said to himself. "If she met me and saw how nice I am, maybe she would want me."

With that he jumped out into the hall, right in front of the little witch. Then he waited for the witch to see him.

"Oh, look!" cried the witch. "Here is a nice little broomstick."

"Well, what a surprise!" said the cat. "You need a broomstick, and here is one, right in this hall."

The witch ran to tell old Mother Witch about finding a broomstick in the hall. "I have a nice little broomstick to ride," she shouted. "It jumped right up to me in the hall of an old house."

"I am glad," said Mother Witch. "It's only a few days now until Halloween, and you needed a broomstick."

When Halloween came, every witch took her broomstick to Mother Witch's house. They met there so they could start away on their sky trip together. "You may ride in pairs," said Mother Witch.

She got on her broomstick and rode off alone to show the way through the sky. The others rode in pairs after her, and away they went to have fun.

How happy the little broom was! "Once I wished for wings, but now I am flying without them," he said.

The Nice Gobbler

Summer was over, and the time came for turkeys to go to market. Every fall farm people sell many turkeys.

As the weeks went by on the big farm, the turkeys became very sad. Before long the farmer would pick out most of them to sell. Then they would leave the farm and start away to market.

One of the best turkeys on the farm was a pretty gobbler. Like the other turkeys, the gobbler wanted to stay on the farm. He did not want to leave.

The farmer came to look at his turkeys. "That is a very nice gobbler," he said, "but he never gobbles. We might keep him if he would gobble for us."

"How strange," said the farmer's boy. "He is a nice gobbler, but he never goes gobble, gobble around the farm."

"Watch him, my boy," said the farmer. "If he ever gobbles, we'll keep him here on the farm. If he never does, we'll sell him with the other turkeys."

The gobbler went away alone to think. "They say that I am nice," he said, "but they don't want me if I cannot gobble. Let me see what I can do."

Then he worked and worked to gobble, but could make no gobble come. "Oh, my!" he cried to himself. "I might as well let them sell me with all the other turkeys. I am not a good gobbler to keep."

In a few more weeks the farmer said,
"You have been watching long enough now.
Has the gobbler ever gobbled?"

"No, Father, he has not gobbled once,"
answered the farmer's boy.

"Then we'll sell him for Thanksgiving,"
said the farmer. "He looks so nice that
I did not want to part with him. Now
he will go with the others."

"Yes, let's sell him for Thanksgiving,"
said the boy. "He will make a good dinner
for someone on Thanksgiving."

That night as the turkeys were sleeping
in a tree, something happened on the farm.
A big fox ran right under the tree where
the turkeys were sleeping. It was coming
to catch some chickens.

The gobbler woke up and saw the fox.
Suddenly he began to gobble. "Why, hear
me gobble," he said. "I'll fly down and
gobble to drive the fox away."

Down he went, "Gobble, gobble, gobble,"
across the barnyard after the old fox.
The fox was so surprised that he started
to run away as fast as he could go.

The farmer heard the noise and came on the run. He came just in time to see the gobbler go, "Gobble, gobble, gobble," after the fox.

"Why, hear that gobbler!" he shouted. "I never heard a gobbler gobble better on a farm before. It takes a good gobbler to drive a fox away."

All this made the farmer very happy. "No one will ever get that good gobbler for Thanksgiving," he said. "He will be right here on Thanksgiving Day."

The gobbler was very happy, too. Now that he could gobble, he would not have to leave the farm. He would not become a Thanksgiving dinner.

On Thanksgiving he gobbled all day. He was saying, "Happy Thanksgiving, happy Thanksgiving to you on this day. It's happy Thanksgiving for me."

Going Upstairs

Mother and I, we made up a game.
   It's "Going Upstairs," we said.
And this is the way we play it,
   Going upstairs to bed:

"I go up one pair of stairs."
   "Just like me."
"I run down the hall."
   "Just like me."
"I open the door."
   "Just like me."
"And there is a nice little girl in bed,
   And it's going to be me."

"One, two, three,
And now we'll see
Just how quick a little girl can be."

In Storyland –
Old Stories

The Sky Is Falling

Once when Henny-Penny was walking, something heavy came down on her head. "Oh, my! The sky is falling," she cried. "I'll run to tell the king."

She dressed in her best clothes and ran to tell the king that the sky was falling. Down the road she raced with never a stop until night. Then she said, "Now I'll sleep, and tomorrow I'll hurry on."

When morning came, she woke up early and started on her way again.

She raced on until she met Cocky-Locky.
"Where are you going this nice morning?"
asked Cocky-Locky.

"Why, I am on my way to see the king,"
called Henny-Penny. "I want to tell him
that the sky is falling."

"Oh, no," said Cocky-Locky, looking up
to see. "Those are only little clouds.
The sky is not falling."

"Yes, it started to fall on my head,"
said Henny-Penny.

"Then I'll run along with you to tell
the king," said Cocky-Locky.

So Cocky-Locky ran along.

"Be quick, be quick," said Henny-Penny, starting away. "We must hurry."

"Yes, we must hurry," said Cocky-Locky, coming along after Henny-Penny.

They went until they met Ducky-Lucky. "You look like funny clowns on parade," said Ducky-Lucky. "Where are you going this nice morning?"

"We are not funny clowns on parade," said Henny-Penny. "We've started to tell the king that the sky is falling."

"Oh, no," said Ducky-Lucky, looking up to see. "Those are only little clouds. The sky is not falling."

"Yes, it started to fall on my head," said Henny-Penny.

"Then I'll run along with you to tell the king," said Ducky-Lucky.

So off raced Henny-Penny, Cocky-Locky, and Ducky-Lucky together.

They went until they met Goosey-Loosey.
"You look like funny clowns on parade,"
said Goosey-Loosey. "Where are you going
this nice morning?"

"We are not funny clowns on parade,"
said Henny-Penny. "We've started to tell
the king that the sky is falling."

"Oh, no," said Goosey-Loosey, looking
up to see. "Those are only little clouds.
The sky is not falling."

"Yes, it started to fall on my head,"
said Henny-Penny.

"Then I'll go along," said Goosey-Loosey.
So off he raced with the others.

They went until they met Turkey-Lurkey.
"You look like funny clowns on parade,"
said Turkey-Lurkey. "Where are you going
this nice morning?"

"We are not funny clowns on parade,"
said Henny-Penny. "We've started to tell
the king that the sky is falling."

"Oh, no," said Turkey-Lurkey, looking
up to see. "Those are only little clouds.
The sky is not falling."

"Yes, it started to fall on my head,"
said Henny-Penny.

"Then I'll go along," said Turkey-Lurkey.
So off he raced with the others.

They went until they met Foxy-Loxy.
"You look like funny clowns on parade,"
said Foxy-Loxy. "Where are you going
this nice morning?"

"We are not funny clowns on parade,"
said Henny-Penny. "We've started to tell
the king that the sky is falling."

"Then come with me," said Foxy-Loxy.
"It's good that you met me. Let me show
you a better way to go."

Henny-Penny, Cocky-Locky, Ducky-Lucky,
Goosey-Loosey, and Turkey-Lurkey started
off with Foxy-Loxy. Before long they came
to a hole with stones around it. "Come in
after me," said Foxy-Loxy.

Now Foxy-Loxy was playing a big trick
on the others. He had a kettle of water
on a fire in the hole. He wanted to catch
them and put them in the kettle to eat.
"M-m-m, m-m," he said to himself.

Henny-Penny looked in the hole and said, "I am afraid to go in. He might catch us and put us in a kettle to eat."

Cocky-Locky said, "Yes, I am afraid to go in the hole, too."

Then they saw Foxy-Loxy with his head part way out of the hole. Just back of him they saw his kettle of water.

Away they went on the run as fast as their legs would carry them. They forgot all about the sky. No one went on to tell the king that the sky was falling.

The Hunter and the Rabbit

A hunter sat by the trunk of an old tree. All at once he saw a rabbit. "I'll catch the rabbit and take him home with me," he said to himself.

"By and by the rabbit will become big," the hunter went on. "Then I'll sell him and get a little pig in his place. Next I'll sell the pig and get a horse.

"The horse will work and help me to get some money," he said. "Then I'll get a cow. The cow will give milk and help me to get more money. After that I'll get chickens and many other animals."

The hunter talked on. "Yes, I'll catch the rabbit and let him get big," he said. "I'll sell him for a pig, and then I'll sell the pig for a horse.

"Next after the horse I'll get a cow," the hunter went on. "They will help me to get money. After that I'll get chickens and many other animals.

"With so many animals I'll have to get a big farm," said the hunter. "I'll plant corn and hay on the farm for my animals. They can eat corn and hay.

"I'll have to build a barn on my farm," he went on. "All the animals will want a place to sleep at night. They can eat corn and hay in the barn."

The hunter was so happy that he talked on and on by the old tree. In a little while he began to shout and sing. "Just think what I can do," he said.

The little rabbit heard the hunter and started to run away. He ran away so fast that the hunter could not catch him. Then the hunter had no rabbit.

The hunter had no pig. He had no horse. He had no cow. He had no chickens. He had no farm, and he had no barn.

He was very sad. "I sat here dreaming and let the rabbit get away," he cried out. "I talked too soon, and I talked too much about things I would do. The next time I'll wait until I have the rabbit."

The Old Shoemaker

Once an old shoemaker had a little store. Every day he worked in his store to make shoes and put them out to sell.

Day after day he said to his wife, "I wish that we had more money. We cannot have a good house. We cannot have good clothes or good things to eat."

"Don't be so sad," said his good wife. "Some day you may have money."

One evening the shoemaker had leather for only one pair of shoes. The next day he would start this pair, and after that his leather would be gone.

He put the leather on an old worktable and got ready for bed. "What shall I do?" he said. "I have only enough leather here for one pair of shoes. Just how can I make shoes without leather?"

"Don't be so sad," said his good wife. "You may get leather after all."

"I don't know how," said the shoemaker. "It takes money to get leather, and I have no money. After I make this pair of shoes, I'll have to find other work."

The next morning the shoemaker said, "We've been poor for a long, long time, my good wife. We've worked and worked, but we've put no money aside. At last, I have no money for leather."

When the shoemaker went into his store, he had a happy surprise waiting for him. In a corner by the chimney he found a pair of shoes ready made.

"Oh, wife," he called. "Someone has made my leather into a good pair of shoes."

Soon a man came into the store to look at the good shoes. He liked them so well that he gave the shoemaker enough money for two pairs of shoes.

"Now you have enough money for leather," said the shoemaker's wife.

The shoemaker ran out to get leather
for two pairs of shoes. That night he put
the leather on his worktable as before.
Then the next morning he found two pairs
of shoes ready made by the chimney.

"How funny!" he said. "Someone makes
shoes for me while I am asleep. They are
very good shoes, too."

Soon people came to the store to look
at the shoes. They liked them so well that
they gave the shoemaker enough money
for four pairs of shoes.

"Again you have money for leather,"
said the shoemaker's wife.

This time the shoemaker brought leather for four pairs of shoes. That night he put the leather on his worktable.

The next morning he found four pairs of shoes ready made beside the chimney. They were good shoes, like all the others that he had found before.

"I'll write a little letter today and leave it on the worktable," said the shoemaker. "I want to thank whoever makes shoes for me at night."

When he went to his store the next day, he found an answer to his letter. It said, "We'll be glad to put shoes by the chimney as long as you need help."

The shoemaker's wife said, "Let's watch to find out who makes the shoes for you. Let's hide to see."

"Yes, my good wife, we'll hide to see," answered the shoemaker.

That night they watched in the store
to find out who made the shoes. What
do you think they saw?

They saw elves come down the chimney
one by one. The elves took off their coats
and climbed up the legs of the table. Then
they started to work.

"Elves! Elves! Oh, see the little elves,"
cried the shoemaker's wife.

"Be quiet, wife," said the shoemaker,
"or the elves will hear you."

The elves worked on and on. At last
they put on their coats and left.

"We should give presents to the elves,"
said the shoemaker's wife. "We might make
teeny-weeny clothes for the elves."

"Let's make little caps and stockings
for them," said the shoemaker. "You make
stockings, and I'll make caps."

"Yes, you make caps, and let me make
stockings," said his wife.

The shoemaker made teeny-weeny caps,
and his wife teeny-weeny stockings. They
put them by the chimney in the store.

That night the elves found their clothes
and put on the little caps and stockings.
Then they played games by the chimney,
and what a time they had!

Chestnuts in the Fire

A cat and a monkey looked at chestnuts in a fire. "I wish that we could get some of them to eat," said the monkey.

"I wish so, too," said the cat. "Maybe we can blow to put the fire out."

The cat began to blow and blow. Then the monkey began to blow and blow, too, but the fire only burned better.

By and by the monkey started to think of other ways to get the chestnuts. Maybe he could trick the cat into pulling them out of the fire. He would say nice things to see what she would do.

"Look, pretty Kitty," said the monkey. "You have nice paws. They are just right for pulling the chestnuts from the fire. Your paws are just right."

The cat was so pleased that she put one of her nice paws into the fire. She pulled out a few chestnuts, but the fire burned all the hair off her paw.

"Oh, Kitty, Kitty," cried the monkey. "How good of you to pull out chestnuts with your nice paw."

The cat was so very proud that she put her other paw into the fire. She pulled out more chestnuts, but the fire burned all the hair off her other paw, too. Now the hair was gone from two paws.

"You pretty Kitty," cried the monkey over and over again.

Time and again the poor cat burned her paws to pull out chestnuts.

The monkey ate the chestnuts as fast as
the cat pulled them out. He did not leave
a one for the cat.

Soon the cat pulled the last chestnut
from the fire. Then she looked and found
no chestnuts around her to eat. "Where
are the chestnuts?" she asked.

"Why, Kitty, I ate them just as fast as
you pulled them out," laughed the monkey.
"I tricked you by nice talk."

All the cat could say at the time was,
"Oh, my poor paws, my poor paws. I have
only burned paws for all this."

The Three Pigs

Once three pigs started away from home.
Soon the first pig met a man with a load
of hay. "Please give me some hay to build
a house," he said.

The pig began to huff and puff to build
his little house. He huffed, and he puffed
as he made the little rooms and chimney.
He wanted a good house.

By and by the little house was ready
for the pig to move in. How happy he was
as he began to live there.

An old wolf walked by the pig's house
and knocked at the door with his big paw.
He beat and beat upon the door. "Quick,
let me come in," he cried.

"Oh, no," cried the pig. "By the hair
on my little chinny-chin-chin, I won't let
you come in."

"By the hair on my big chinny-chin-chin,
I'll huff, and I'll puff, and I'll blow
your house in," cried the wolf.

So the old wolf huffed, and he puffed
by the hair on his big chinny-chin-chin.
Soon the house went to pieces.

The pig started to run from the house,
but the wolf soon held him in his paws.
"Let me go," cried the pig.

"Oh, no, I want to eat you for dinner,"
laughed the wolf.

Then the old wolf ate the little pig
and started on his way.

The next pig came to a man with a load
of sticks. He made a house of sticks.

Soon the old wolf knocked at the door
with his paw. As he beat upon the door,
he said, "Quick, let me come in."

"Oh, no," cried the pig. "By the hair
on my little chinny-chin-chin, I won't let
you come in."

"By the hair on my big chinny-chin-chin,
I'll huff, and I'll puff, and I'll blow
your house in," cried the wolf.

So the old wolf huffed, and he puffed
by the hair on his big chinny-chin-chin,
and the house went to pieces. Then he ate
the little pig for dinner.

The other pig made his house of stone.
The wolf knocked on the door as before
and said, "Quick, let me come in."

"Oh, no," cried the pig. "By the hair
on my little chinny-chin-chin, I won't let
you come in."

"By the hair on my big chinny-chin-chin,
I'll huff, and I'll puff, and I'll blow
your house in," cried the wolf.

So the old wolf huffed, and he puffed
by the hair on his big chinny-chin-chin,
but he could not blow the house down.
At last he went away.

"I cannot blow the pig's house down,"
said the old wolf, "but I can trick him,
I can, I can."

So he called to the pig, "I know where
you can get good vegetables and apples
to eat in your house."

"Where?" asked the pig.

"On Farmer Gray's farm," said the wolf.
"Early tomorrow morning I'll stop for you,
and we'll go there together. We'll go to get
vegetables and apples."

Now the pig saw that the wolf wished
to trick him. So he got up before daylight
and went away to the farm all by himself.
After a while he came back with a basket
of vegetables and apples.

By the time the wolf came to the house,
the pig was eating vegetables and apples.
"You did not wait for me," said the wolf.
"I'll trick you some other time."

The next day it rained. The wolf came
in the rain and said, "Little pig, let's go
to town. I'll get my umbrella and come
to take you to town."

As soon as the wolf left, the pig got out
his umbrella and started off to town alone.
He went all alone in the rain.

On the way home he saw the wolf coming
along the road. Quick as could be, he got
into the umbrella to hide. Then suddenly
the umbrella started to roll.

When the wolf saw the umbrella rolling,
he started to run away. He was so afraid
that he ran all the way home.

After this the wolf wanted all the more
to get the pig. "I'll go down the chimney
of his house to get him," he said.

The pig saw the old wolf in the chimney
and put wood on the fire. Over the fire
he put a big kettle of water.

Now the old wolf was caught in a trap,
for he could not climb out. Before long
he started to fall. Down, down he rolled
right into the kettle of water.

"Ha, ha, ha," laughed the little pig,
for that was the last of the wolf.

Good-by, Book Friends

Little book friends, from far and wide,
  From city, town, and countryside,
We've had much fun in meeting you
  And seeing all the things you do.

We've seen you work, we've seen you play
  As we've gone with you day by day.
What we have seen has helped us find
  Good things to know of every kind.

And now before we leave this book,
  We turn again for one more look.
Then thank you and good-by we say.
  Let's meet again another day.

TO THE TEACHER

Meet Our Friends is the basic second reader of the "Reading for Living Series." The content is made up of stories grouped into units, each with a central controlling theme. The first four units are primarily experience units, portraying realistic co-operative experiences of children living in typical community environments, urban, village, and rural. The two remaining units are chiefly literary units, one a collection of carefully selected modern stories and the other a collection of choice old stories. Each unit in the book contains a poem, sufficiently simple in vocabulary and meaning to be read by the child.

The vocabulary, as listed below, includes 236 new words. In addition, it includes all 58 words originally introduced in the pre-primers, all 102 words originally introduced in the primer, and all 176 words originally introduced in the first reader. Only two new words are introduced on any page, and each has strong initial use, being repeated on the page of introduction or the first page thereafter. All new words are repeated systematically through the book, being used at least 10 times. All old words are used at least 5 times in the book. Variants are consistently counted as new words except (1) the *s* form of nouns, verbs, and a few scattered pronouns; (2) the *d*, *ed*, and *ing* forms of verbs; (3) the possessive *s* form of nouns, used rather sparingly; (4) compounds made up of known words or known compounds broken into words.

1	Pine	18	new		speak	53	say
	Square		knocked	34	roll		automobile
2	ice	19	......		clapped	54	road
	cream	20	sick	35	......		Main
3	let's		cold	36	......	55	wide
	tag	21	bed	37	......		place
4	caught		better	38	picked	56	bunk
	could	22	woke	39	tomorrow	57	......
5	heard		stay		think	58	Timmie
	ting-a-ling	23	blocks	40	I'll	59	game
6	much	24	......		brown	60	Saturday
7	......	25	hope	41	almost		week
8	lived	26	brought		left	61	turns
	men		table	42	smile		low
9	pet	27	black	43	......	62	......
10	while		gloves	44	climbed	63	strange
11	truck	28	gone	45	high	64	groceries
	washing		must	46	......		we'll
12	suddenly	29	waved	47	if	65	......
13	loud		those	48	rode	66	corner
14	took	30	hands	49	......		sell
15	Peter		bark	50	move	67	packages
	tent	31	held		town	68	well
16	just	32	Pepper	51	small	69	......
	crash		most		many	70	Monday
17	hurt	33	sat	52	......	71	......

72 building
green
73 found
write
74 about
75 ......
76 lost
77 seen
spots
78 ears
nose
79 legs
feet
80 ......
81 drive
hitched
82 grass
waiting
83 glad
84 should
85 ......
86 meet
87 ......
88 ......
89 scratch
wings
90 ......
91 winter
92 lights
93 ......
94 together
95 ......
96 ......
97 ......
98 railroad
99 station
tickets
100 through
101 ......
102 visit
103 ......
104 ......
105 it's
106 sky
107 talking
songs
108 front
109 Jones
110 traffic
111 these
112 engine
loads
113 sailor
114 ......
115 stones
need

116 ......
117 Mike
tractor
118 ......
119 afraid
120 faster
clouds
121 ground
stack
122 ......
123 stories
124 trailer
trips
125 river
bridge
126 cross
127 ......
128 ......
129 ......
130 telephone
131 leave
132 answered
133 don't
134 ......
135 ......
136 corn
plowing
137 huff
puff
138 ......
139 before
140 ......
141 ducks
hen
142 does
143 ......
144 ......
145 ......
146 garden
summer
147 part
vegetables
148 never
149 poor
any
150 ......
151 plants
been
152 ......
153 ......
154 ......
155 might
quiet
156 pieces
fur
157 ......
158 own

159 ......
160 ......
161 alone
sad
162 chair
163 ......
164 ......
165 ......
166 proud
read
167 land
168 ......
169 ......
170 ......
171 because
172 evening
pumpkin
173 enough
right
174 pie
175 ......
176 ......
177 ......
178 clock
ticktock
179 crackle
snap
180 self
181 kettle
182 ha
183 ......
184 singing
185 tail
186 goes
187 ......
188 mock
189 ......
190 elf
hide
191 few
happened
192 mice
catch
193 traps
194 ......
195 ever
196 ......
197 peddler
caps
198 head
colors
199 until
200 ......
201 ......
202 ......
203 Easter

204 pink
fall
205 break
206 Humpty Dumpty
quick
207 ......
208 ......
209 broom
Halloween
210 ......
211 hall
witch
212 met
pair
213 nice
214 ......
215 gobbler
turkeys
216 gobbles
217 Thanks-
giving
218 ......
219 ......
220 ......
221 ......
222 king
223 ......
224 we've
225 ......
226 ......
227 ......
228 ......
229 hunter
230 ......
231 ......
232 shoemaker
wife
233 leather
234 chimney
235 ......
236 ......
237 elves
238 ......
239 chestnuts
blow
240 paws
hair
241 ......
242 ......
243 wolf
244 ......
245 ......
246 ......
247 ......
248 ......
249 ......

ACKNOWLEDGMENTS

Grateful credit is given to the following authors and publishers for permission to adapt and use copyrighted materials:

Dorothy W. Baruch for "Merry-Go-Round" from *I Like Machinery*, published by Harper & Brothers; Marion Marsh Brown for "Mike Takes a Sky Ride" adapted from the story, which appeared in *Highlights for Children; Child Life* for "An Elf Plays Tricks" adapted from "Peter Podpuff" by Wyn Alford; Mort Cornin for "Mr. Jones and His Truck" adapted from "Jasper Jones and His Trailer Truck," which appeared in *Jack and Jill;* Ethel J. Eldridge for "The Baby Ducks" adapted from "Dickie and Mugsy on the Farm" and for "What Visits the Garden?" adapted from "The Visiting Rabbits," both of which appeared in *American Childhood; The Grade Teacher*, Darien, Conn., for "Blue Mr. Blue" adapted from the story by A. Schroder, which appeared in the April 1948 issue, and for "The Proud Cow" adapted from the story by Mary Luckey Sharkey, which appeared in the June 1947 issue; Robert L. Grimes for "The Birds' Singing Party" adapted from "Mr. Long-Tail's Music Book"; Harper & Brothers for "Groceries" from *I Live in a City* by James S. Tippett, copyright, 1927, by Harper & Brothers; Mark Hawkins for "Jean and the Funny Animals" adapted from "Merry-Go-Round," which appeared in the *American Junior Red Cross News;* Dorothy Z. Johnson for "Little Lost Cat" adapted from "Little Cat Lost," which appeared in *Jack and Jill;* Marjorie Larson for "The Funny Old Clock" adapted from "The Clock That Wouldn't Say Tick-Tock," which appeared in *Jack and Jill;* Emma H. Lawton for "The Happy Little Broom" adapted from "The Littlest Broom," which appeared in *American Childhood;* Jane Marquette for "A Strange Kind of Horse"; F. A. Owen Publishing Company for "Peter's One Big Wish" adapted from "Peter Pumpkin's Wish" by Ruby L. Chandler, and for "Black Pepper" adapted from the story by Laura Morrison, both of which appeared in *The Instructor; Plays* for "The Eggs in Pretty Colors" adapted from "The Little Pink Egg" by Claribel Spamer, copyright by Plays, Inc., originally appeared in *Plays, The Drama Magazine for Young People;* Miriam Clark Potter for "Here Comes the Bus" adapted from the story, which appeared in *Jack and Jill;* Solveig Paulson Russell for "The Nice Gobbler" adapted from "The Gobbler Who Would Not Gobble," which appeared in *Highlights for Children;* William R. Scott, Inc., for "The Surprised Peddler" adapted from *Caps for Sale* by Esphyr Slobodkina; Charles Scribner's Sons for "Going Upstairs" reprinted from *Open the Door* by Marion Edey and Dorothy Grider, copyright, 1949, by Marion Edey and Dorothy Grider, used by permission of the publishers, Charles Scribner's Sons.

Appreciative recognition also is extended to the artists, Janet Ross and Raymon Naylor. Janet Ross prepared illustrations for the preliminary pages, unit title pages, and the stories from pages 2 to 176. Raymon Naylor prepared illustrations for the stories from pages 178 to 249.